LIFE, LIBERTY, AND PROPERTY

Essays on Locke's Political Ideas

D1255385

WADSWORTH STUDIES IN PHILOSOPHICAL CRITICISM

Alexander Sesonke, General Editor

HUMAN UNDERSTANDING:
Studies in the Philosophy of David Hume

META-*MEDITATIONS*:
Studies in Descartes

PLATO'S *MENO*:
Text and Criticism

PLATO'S *REPUBLIC*:
Interpretation and Criticism

LIMITS OF LIBERTY:
Studies of Mill's *On Liberty*

ARISTOTLE'S *ETHICS*:
Issues and Interpretations

BERKELEY'S *PRINCIPLES OF HUMAN KNOWLEDGE*:
Critical Studies

HOBBES'S *LEVIATHAN*:
Interpretation and Criticism

MILL'S *UTILITARIANISM*:
Text and Criticism

THE FIRST CRITIQUE:
Reflections on Kant's *Critique of Pure Reason*

LIFE, LIBERTY, AND PROPERTY:
Essays on Locke's Political Ideas

LIFE, LIBERTY, AND PROPERTY

Essays on Locke's Political Ideas

Gordon J. Schochet

LIVINGSTON COLLEGE,
RUTGERS UNIVERSITY

Wadsworth Publishing Company, Inc.
BELMONT, CALIFORNIA

WADSWORTH STUDIES IN PHILOSOPHICAL CRITICISM

The idea of a series of Studies in Philosophical Criticism developed in response to a growing problem in American universities. Philosophy can be taught most successfully in small classes; philosophical understanding grows in the course of a dialogue where problems are discussed from diverse points of view by men who differ in experience and temperament. But with the increase in college enrollments, the size of introductory classes has grown larger and the possibility of a dialogue between professor and students more remote. Our hope is that the Studies in Philosophical Criticism will make a dialogue of sorts possible in a class of a hundred, or a thousand, as well as in smaller classes and seminars. Each volume in the series contains a collection of critical writings related to a single classical philosophical text, such as Descartes' *Meditations* or Plato's *Republic*. These critical writings are not substitutes for the classical work, but supplements to it. They should be read in conjunction with the classical text. So used, they will bring to bear on the problems raised by Descartes, Hume, or Plato that diversity of voices and viewpoints which is the heart of the dialogue—and also, we hope, will prompt the student to add his voice to the discussion.

In selecting material for the volumes in the series, the editors have not searched primarily for writings which provide a definitive analysis of the classical text, but have rather selected those papers they thought might be most useful in undergraduate courses in philosophy, both to provoke students into serious engagement with the text and the problems found there, and to present them with a variety of philosophical styles and idioms. Most of the writings reprinted are quite contemporary; they were selected not only for their excellence but also as an indication that many of the classical problems of philosophy persist as centers of current controversy. We believe this format also achieves one prime desideratum: it acquaints the student with both the great works of the philosophical tradition and the most contemporary concepts, techniques, and modes of thought.

CONTENTS

INTRODUCTION
1

W. von Leyden
JOHN LOCKE AND NATURAL LAW
12

Leo Strauss
LOCKE AND THE MODERN THEORY OF
NATURAL RIGHT
26

Charles H. Monson, Jr.
LOCKE AND HIS INTERPRETERS
33

William J. Wainwright
NATURAL RIGHTS
49

C. B. Macpherson
THE SOCIAL BEARING OF LOCKE'S
POLITICAL THEORY
60

Alan Ryan
LOCKE AND THE DICTATORSHIP OF
THE BOURGEOISIE
86

J. P. Day
LOCKE ON PROPERTY
107

E. F. Carritt

POLITICAL OBLIGATION AS MORALITY

124

John Dunn

CONSENT IN THE POLITICAL THEORY OF
JOHN LOCKE

129

Richard I. Aaron

AUTHORITY AND THE RIGHTS OF INDIVIDUALS

162

Willmoore Kendall

THE RIGHT OF THE MAJORITY

168

SUGGESTED FURTHER READINGS

179

INTRODUCTION

John Locke is widely regarded as the philosophic godfather of the American political creed. It is a commonplace assumption that the noble ideals of Jefferson's Declaration of Independence were inspired by the sentiments and the very phrases of Locke's *Two Treatises on Government*.[1] The central thesis of Louis Hartz's influential and stimulating *The Liberal Tradition in America* (New York: Harcourt, Brace, 1955) is that our political institutions and liberal predispositions and traditions are a result of our Lockean consensus. Indeed, it is because of this acceptance of Locke, Hartz suggests, that America developed in the way that it did.[2] Locke is very much a part of our political consciousness, and we proudly trill off those of his principles that mean so much to us—natural law and natural rights, the sacredness and inviolability of private property, the consent of the governed, and the right of revolution—and commit to memory the notion that our nation was born in defense of these Lockean doctrines and is dedicated to their preservation. However, a careful reading of Locke's actual words reveals both that Locke himself was not nearly so clear as our beliefs about him would suggest and that he may not even have said some of the things attributed to him. The essays reprinted in this collection have been chosen in part to illustrate these ambiguities in both Locke and modern interpretations of his thought.

It is, of course, impossible to examine all of the important questions arising from the *Two Treatises*. The selections presented here deal primarily with the presumed Lockean principles that are associated with the United States. More generally, they introduce Locke's political thought and some of the fundamental problems of political philosophy itself; in addition, these articles provide a picture of Locke

[1] See the discussion in Carl L. Becker's highly regarded *The Declaration of Independence: A Study in the History of Political Ideas* (New York: Alfred A. Knopf, 1942), Ch. 2.

[2] The notion that Locke was actually a significant influence on the American political mind in its formative period has been challenged in brilliant fashion and with most impressive scholarship; see John Dunn, "The Politics of Locke in England and America in the Eighteenth Century," *John Locke: Problems and Perspectives (A Collection of New Essays)*, ed. John W. Yolton (Cambridge, England: Cambridge University Press, 1969), pp. 45–80.

scholarship. As Charles Monson observes in the third essay, there has been a lively and growing interest in Locke in recent years, and especially in his political thought. The number of works on Locke has continued to increase rapidly since 1958, when Monson's essay was originally published. Among the reasons for this attention is a renewed concern about political philosophy, a subject that had been very much neglected in the period after World War II. As the relationship of man and the political order assumes a greater importance for us, it is understandable that we should be drawn back to Locke, Rousseau, John Stuart Mill, and other seminal thinkers whose places in the development of the "liberal-democratic" tradition have always been secure. They are important to us today because the world we wish to understand (and/or to change) is in part their creation and must be approached in their terms.

A further stimulus to Locke scholarship has been the availability—since about 1952—of Locke's personal papers, which include many letters, extensive reading notes and journals, numerous book lists, and manuscripts of political and philosophic essays that were never published. These materials have proved extremely valuable in showing the evolution of Locke's doctrines and in helping to clarify a number of major ambiguities in his published works. Accordingly, the manuscripts have made it possible for scholars to question some of the standard interpretations, which has generally encouraged the expansion of Locke studies. The "new" Locke who is emerging from the analysis of his papers is very closely related to the England of the middle to late seventeenth century, for any attempt to understand a man's philosophic or political doctrine in terms of the books he read, the letters he wrote, the controversies in which he engaged, and his presumed purposes in writing must necessarily concentrate upon the historical context. The words an author used and the meanings they had to him and others *at the time he wrote*—as revealed in his own papers, in the writings of his contemporaries, or in the unconsciously held ideologies that were then current—become essential ingredients for understanding historical texts. Of the essays reprinted here, those by Von Leyden, Macpherson, and Dunn are most conspicuously wedded to this method of interpretation, but only Dunn discusses some of the consequences of approaching Locke from the perspective of seventeenth century history rather than from that of twentieth century politics and philosophy. A contrary position claims that there is an important sense in which we are permitted to read Locke (or any other historical author, for that matter) in terms of our own interests and outlooks. Just as there are a number of persistent themes in political philosophy, so there may be ways in which Locke "transcended" the specific problems of his own age and dealt with issues that are relevant to all historical periods. This claim is most clearly found— again, implicitly rather than self-consciously—in the articles by Strauss, Monson, Wainwright, Day, and Carritt.

This methodological difference is perhaps the major question currently being debated by historians of philosophy and political thought, and we cannot go much further with the issue here. Suffice it to say that there are virtues in both contentions, and many of these strengths are highlighted by the articles in this collection.

All of these articles presuppose a familiarity with at least the "Second Treatise," for they are generally interpretive rather than simply expository, and the interpretations can usually be questioned on either philosophic or historical grounds and in some cases on both. Even in terms of the methodological problems just discussed, different and conflicting readings of Locke's meaning are not only possible but perfectly legitimate. It is in part this richness and profundity and a level of meaning that defies a first or a superficial reading that distinguish works of political philosophy from mere political tracts and still make Locke's *Two Treatises* valuable. To read and understand Locke and to appreciate the controversies that are represented in this anthology are to begin to grasp something about the nature of political philosophy and to participate in a discourse that extends back to Plato and as far forward in time as we can contemplate. Thus, most of these articles do more than interpret John Locke; they criticize and praise the *Two Treatises*, move beyond the text and attempt to apply and expand some of its principles, and formulate propositions in political philosophy proper and not just about its history.

One of the central and persistent concerns of political philosophy has always been the search for objective and universal standards with which to justify the political order. Such standards, if they could be identified, would apply to all cultures and societies. These inalterable, absolute principles would not depend upon men for their validity or existence but would be part of the very nature of the world; they would be correct and binding whether men accepted them or not. The name "natural law" is often given to this suprahuman moral order. In the first essay, W. von Leyden offers an analysis of Locke's theory of natural law, which he sees as the basis for Locke's moral and political views. Von Leyden uses Locke's conception of natural law to point out some common elements in the *Two Treatises*, the *Essay concern-*

ing Human Understanding (Locke's best known philosophic work), and some early writings on the natural law by Locke that Von Leyden himself has recently edited and translated. One of the most famous (but least understood) portions of *Human Understanding* is a detailed criticism of the theory of "innate ideas" that was popular in the seventeenth century (*Human Understanding*, Bk. I). According to a very simple and naive version of this doctrine, there are some "truths" or principles that are implanted in men's souls or minds and which are thus known to them independently of sensory experiences. It is often suggested that Locke's refutation of this view is also applicable to the conception of natural law in the *Two Treatises*. Von Leyden persuasively argues, on the contrary, that in the context of seventeenth century philosophy, the acceptance of natural law does not conflict with the denial of innate ideas. Some of the difficulties inherent in all natural law and rationalistic political theories are indicated by Von Leyden. One important problem that remains, however, is the status in terms of *Human Understanding* of those passages in the "Second Treatise" in which Locke said that the law of nature was "writ in the hearts of all mankind" and was "no where to be found but in the minds of men" (sections 11 and 136). In at least these two places, Locke seems to have come very close to deriving natural law from innate knowledge. Note finally that Von Leyden implicitly says that the concept "natural law" is a historical notion that changes both its meaning and its content within different settings.

In the next selection—which is taken from one of the most controversial studies of Locke in many years—Leo Strauss argues that Locke did not have a conception of natural law at all. It is Strauss's contention, based upon close reading of several of Locke's works, that what passes for a moral natural law in the Lockean system is actually equivalent to the nonmoral "prudential maxims" of Thomas Hobbes. Locke tried to disguise his closeness to Hobbes, according to Strauss, by scattering his meaning throughout his works and by gradually shifting his arguments. This interpretation is not historical, and it has been criticized for precisely this failure to read Locke in the context of seventeenth century England. In order to make his case, Strauss argues that a single, consistent doctrine can be extracted from Locke's writings.

Charles Monson introduces some of the complexities in Locke's political philosophy by criticizing Strauss and other scholars who claim to have identified the central and persistent doctrine of the *Two Treatises*. His essay concludes with an interesting reduction of Locke's position to three basic but contradictory principles—consent, freedom, and equality. These same doctrines, Monson argues, with their attendant inconsistencies and difficulties, are also found in the theory of contemporary democracy. While his general position supports my claim that the relationship between Locke and the present needs to be reevaluated, Monson's easy and virtually unnoticeable movement from the seventeenth to the twentieth century should not be unhesitatingly accepted.

The theory of "natural rights"—which bears an important resemblance to natural law—is directly linked to Locke. According to this doctrine, certain rights that do not depend upon governmental institution for their existence are common to all men; each man is morally required to respect the natural rights of everyone else. One of the main purposes of the political order is to see that these rights are protected, and a major limitation on government is its inability to transgress or interfere with natural rights. However, as the essay by William Wainwright illustrates, the very notion of natural rights is rather vague. Wainwright attempts to construct an acceptable and consistent conception of natural rights and then argues that Locke's formulation will not satisfy it.

The next three essays examine Locke's celebrated theory of property. Locke regarded property as a natural right, but he used the term "property" in at least three different senses. (1) Sometimes he treated property as goods and possessions, including the landed property that we mean today when we call a lot or tract of land a "piece of property." And occasionally, Locke seems to have meant only landed goods. (2) Often Locke talked of the property that one has in himself and his activities (including his work). (3) Finally, Locke frequently spoke of property as "life, liberty, and estate." The difficulty is that arguments appropriate to property in one sense were sometimes used by Locke to discuss and justify property in either of the other two senses; these distinctions must be kept in mind when reading these three articles and when trying to understand Locke's meaning. It is, of course, as the defender of property as goods and land that Locke is important to the United States and is often taken as one of the chief architects of the theory of modern capitalism. Proponents of a capitalist economy find in Locke a defense of their own position and a demonstration of the dependence of a democratic political order on the right of private property.

C. B. Macpherson regards Locke's theory as the very basis for aggressive, individualist, capitalist accumulation. He sees the doctrine of the *Two Treatises* as essentially antiegalitarian and antimajoritarian. Basing his analysis upon Locke's often unstated assumptions—which, he holds, were implicit in the late seventeenth century intellectual climate within which the *Two Treatises* were conceived and written— Macpherson concludes that Locke provided the moral basis and justification for a bourgeois, class state. This argument is most impressive, not least in its very precise use of Locke's words to illustrate its contentions. The theory that Macpherson has found in Locke is undoubtedly an individualistic defense of the rights of private ownership, and it is certainly true that this doctrine resembles the philosophic supports of contemporary capitalism. But Alan Ryan argues that Macpherson has relied upon too many ambiguous passages and has imposed an unwarranted consistency upon the *Two Treatises;* in the end, Ryan contends, the notion of class domination follows less clearly from Locke's text than does the more traditional, egalitarian interpretation. (Note also Ryan's important distinction between what Locke "intended" and what he "said.") In the final discussion of property in the *Two Treatises,* J. P. Day argues that Locke's theory is fundamentally erroneous because of a failure to distinguish between several senses of "work" and "labor." Day's article is probably the most difficult essay in this collection, but it is both interesting and worthwhile as an application of some contemporary philosophic methods to an important historical problem.

Locke's theory of political obligation—that is, the grounds on which the duty to obey the state can be justified—is fully discussed by E. F. Carritt, who stresses the mutuality of moral relationships as the basis of obligation for Locke and minimizes the role of the "contractual" and consent theories. Carritt is attempting to remove Locke from the utilitarian tradition in which obligation is related to (perceived) self-interest and "happiness." This understanding of Locke's conception of obligation as based upon moral principles rather than prudence should certainly be compared to the essay by John Dunn.[3] Macpherson, of course, would disagree with Carritt and contend that obligation for Locke *was* indistinguishable from interest. The purpose of the state—as Macpherson reads Locke—is to protect property, which is a kind of interest, and the duty to obey is a result of that protection.

This dispute can never be finally resolved, for Locke's text will

---

[3] See also Hanna Pitkin, "Obligation and Consent—I," *American Political Science Review,* Vol. 59 (1964), esp. 994–997.

substantiate both interpretations. The larger question that emerges from this juxtaposition of Carritt and Macpherson goes considerably beyond Locke to the very problem of political obligation itself. Is it ever possible to talk satisfactorily of an obligation to obey political authority that is founded upon something other than interest? If so, what is it that justifies obligation, and how can it be recognized? If, for instance, it is agreed that we are morally required to obey a "just" state, who is to define "justice" so that we may actually *know* when we are obligated? And what becomes of the very notion of "justice" if we honestly disagree with some authoritative statement about what constitutes "justice" or whether a particular state is "just" but are compelled to obey nonetheless? If, on the other hand, obligation does indeed follow from interest, what happens when individual interests conflict? Or are we to distinguish between "apparent" (and possibly false) and "real" (and always genuine) interests? It is certainly true that men are sometimes mistaken about what is good for them, but is it not a departure from the principle of interest to establish an agency that authoritatively determines men's "real" interests and thereby directs them to their political obligations? These questions about the nature of political authority actually define the problem of political obligation. And to the extent that a society or political philosophy seeks to preserve a realm of personal moral autonomy and responsibility, the imposition of authority will always introduce tensions.

Locke did not succeed in resolving these tensions, but his theory of consent—which Carritt believes is relatively unimportant—can be seen as an attempt to deal with the problem of authority. The consent doctrine is usually interpreted as meaning that an individual is obligated to obey the state because he has consented to its authority and has agreed to be bound by its (legitimate) decisions. Waiving the problems inherent in defining "legitimate," the central difficulty with this thesis is that many people have not actually consented. It cannot be that these individuals owe no allegiance to the state, but on what grounds can they be regarded as obligated? Locke recognized this dilemma and introduced "tacit consent." According to this principle— which is popular among proponents of the consent theory of obligation in the United States[4]—there are certain acts such as inheriting

---

[4] See, for instance, Joseph Tussman, *Obligation and the Body Politic* (New York: Oxford University Press, 1960), and Alan Gewirth, "Political Justice," *Social Justice*, ed. Richard B. Brandt (Englewood Cliffs, N.J.: Prentice-Hall, 1962), pp. 128 ff.

property and accepting the services and protections of the state[5] that constitute tacit or silent consent. There are many difficulties and ambiguities in Locke's theory of tacit consent, not least among them that tacit consent would impose the same duty to obey the state upon the would-be revolutionary as upon the son who voluntarily inherited his father's property and thereby expressly consented. However, the question that Locke seems to leave open—perhaps because it did not occur to him to raise it—is the validity of relating political obligation to overt or express consent.

An altogether different approach is urged by John Dunn, who says—in the most thorough analysis of Locke's theory of consent that has yet been published—that political obligation and consent raise separate questions for Locke. The confusion stems from the fact that we do not distinguish these issues today and have continually analyzed Locke from our own ideological perspective, which he did not share with us but which, ironically, we regard as "Lockean." Consequently, we feel justified both in searching for the components of "Lockean politics" in the *Two Treatises* and in criticizing Locke himself when he fails to deal adequately with the questions we put to him. We do not notice that we have given distinctly twentieth century and secular meanings to "consent" and "political obligation." It is our belief, Dunn continues, that "because you consented" is a standard (though possibly incorrect) answer to "Why should I obey the state?" But for Locke as Dunn interprets him, the reason for obeying is theological; political obligation is part of a more fundamental duty to obey God. Consent, on the other hand, is not directly related to obligation; it provides an answer to the question "How did I become a member of this state?" which Dunn seems to imply is distinguishable from the reasons for obeying it.

The two final essays focus principally on the extent to which Locke may be regarded as an individualist political philosopher. Rich-

---

[5] This is often extended by contemporary thinkers to include participating in some political process, especially elections, but it is not apparent that Locke would have regarded participation as an act of tacit consent. Since participation is limited to members of a political society, it would seem that some act of consent should *precede* voting. One of the confusions here to which too little attention has been paid is that two different questions are included in the consent theory: how one becomes a *member* of a state and why one is *obliged* to obey it. Locke distinguished these questions, limiting membership to those who had *expressly* consented. All members were obligated by virtue of their membership; nonmembers incurred their obligations by giving tacit consent, and while they had many of the same *duties* as members, they presumably lacked the *rights* of membership. For further discussion, see the essay by John Dunn.

ard Aaron raises the question of sovereignty, which itself is not one of the central issues in the *Two Treatises;* however, it leads to other more important problems. After discussing the varying roles of the monarch, the legislature, and people, Aaron concludes that Locke's treatment was vague and contradictory. Some of the confusions to which he calls attention are similar to the difficulties noted by Monson. Aaron sees a doctrine of popular sovereignty in Locke, which in turn is said to be a result of thoroughgoing individualism: each person is a distinct individual with his own rights, freedoms, and interests. The state cannot interfere with these aspects of individualism; indeed, the political order is an instrumentality created primarily to defend them (compare Macpherson's interpretation). When the state fails to provide this protection, according to Aaron, resistance is justified. Although he recognizes that the freedom of one man is limited by that of another, and while he also sees that it may sometimes be necessary and justifiable to curtail the rights of one person to advance those of someone else, Aaron does not raise the question of authority: how, by whom, and according to what standards are these judgments of conflict resolution to be made?

Willmoore Kendall attempts to sort out this very important issue and argues that Locke was not a champion of personal rights at all but was a majoritarian. The upshot of this reading of Locke is that the individual is required to follow the wishes of the majority and, in fact, has no right of revolution—unless a majority of the members of a civil society share his grievance and are willing to act upon it. But in such cases, a simple political maneuver of electing and installing new governmental officials would generally be all that was needed. Active resistance would be necessary only in those instances where the government was opposed by the majority but refused to change its policies or to surrender control. But such an order would be despotic and would not fall within the political system Locke is describing. ("Absolute dominion," Locke wrote in section 174 of the "Second Treatise," "however placed, is so far from being one kind of civil society, that it is as inconsistent with it, as slavery is with property." See also sections 90 and 137.)

If Kendall's interpretation is correct—and there is much in the text of the "Second Treatise" to support it—Locke has provided the basis for majoritarian tyranny. In these terms, an oppressed minority that is unable to convince a majority of the citizens of its plight and to persuade them to alter the policies of the government has no defensible recourse within the system. If this is the case, we are entitled to ask once more, What is the point of the consensual account of obligation?

If I am required to obey the state because I consented to its authority but cannot withdraw my consent and thereby cancel my obligation when I no longer feel that authority is justified, very little has been gained by deriving my duty to obey from my agreement. I am as firmly bound to the wishes of the rulers—so long as they are supported by the majority—as if God had ordered me to obey "the powers that be." (This difficulty provides a further argument in support of Dunn's attempt to separate political obligation from consent.) If we pursue Kendall's interpretation of Locke, the fact that a majority may legitimately alter political authority does not change my relationship to the state, for I am still morally bound to whatever rulers are accepted by the majority regardless of my own attitudes and regardless of whether my personal property is being protected.

A further situation not covered by the Locke who emerges from Kendall's reading is one in which the government is actually destroying the rights and interests of the majority but through the use of propaganda or some other means has been able to conceal this fact. Such a regime will retain the support of most of the people, who will genuinely believe that their lives, liberties, and estates are being protected. In other words, are we entitled to look beyond mere attitudes and to distinguish, once again, between "real" and "apparent" interests, or is the interest of the majority whatever the majority perceives it to be regardless of the sources of that perception and its correspondence to "reality"?

If, on the other hand, we accept the implications of Aaron's individualist reading of Locke, we are open to the possibility of perpetual anarchy. If each person is entitled to judge for himself when his rights and interests are being protected by the government and to resist when he honestly feels they are being abused, we have returned to the state of nature with its lack of an enforceable law. It was precisely this condition and its attendant inconveniences—including disagreements among men of genuine goodwill—that Locke's political order was designed to overcome. Such conflicts, Locke suggested, are inevitable whenever men interact. Thus, politics necessarily involves the institutionalization of the means whereby men can, from time to time, be persuaded (and perhaps compelled) to give up what they *regard* as their interests because of some presumably greater good or the overriding claim of a competing interest. But there must be rules according to which these decisions are made and principles or standards in terms of which the rules are applied. Who is to make these rules and to oversee their enforcement? Locke seems to have provided two incompatible answers, neither of which is satisfactory, the majority and each individual for himself. Majoritarianism destroys the personal rights and interests that the principle of compromise is designed to maintain. Individualism is destructive of the society that is established and preserved by the peaceful resolution of conflicts.

We have, then, come full circle. The doctrines in Locke's political philosophy upon which the American democratic creed has presumably been founded have been seen to be nonexistent, sufficiently vague to permit conflicting interpretations, or irrelevant to our present circumstances. Locke simply will not support the burden we have attempted to place upon him. Three conclusions follow from these realizations. In the first place, if we actually wish to preserve the political principles we have long associated with Locke, we should strive to find viable "foundations" for them. Second, the discovery that some of these doctrines are extremely complex and perhaps untenable—as Locke's treatments reveal—should persuade us of the need to rethink our principles and to pay careful attention to their contents and implications and, hopefully, should show us how to modify or perhaps even abandon some of them. Finally, once we have stopped trying to extract from (or foist upon) the *Two Treatises* the whole of contemporary liberal democracy, we may get down to the business of understanding Locke himself and in his own terms. It is undoubtedly true that Locke contributed to the "tradition of political philosophy." But his contribution was peculiarly his own, and it is from this perspective that he must finally be appreciated. He is no worn-out ideologue whom we should jettison at our pleasure, but neither is he an all-wise and all-seeing prophet whom we ignore at our peril.

NOTE

The best edition of Locke's *Two Treatises* is the one by Peter Laslett, which is available in an inexpensive paperback edition (Mentor). Laslett's edition contains an excellent introduction and notes to the text which are based upon thorough analyses of Locke's manuscripts.

The essays reprinted in this collection are not of uniform difficulty. While I have designed the collection to be read straight through, students with no previous knowledge of Locke or of political philosophy could change the order with no serious loss. A suggested rearrangement for such students—in order of increasing difficulty—would be Monson, Macpherson, Ryan, Aaron, Kendall, Von Leyden, Wainwright, Carritt, Dunn, Strauss, and Day.

JOHN LOCKE AND
NATURAL LAW*

W. von Leyden

It has been said, and few would deny, that John Locke is as important as the founder of philosophical liberalism as he is as the founder of the empiricist theory of knowledge. Though he was a most versatile thinker, writing on philosophy, politics, medicine, education, religion, and economics, and on all these with the knowledge of an expert and the influence of an authority, his fame no doubt derives on the one hand from his treatises on Toleration and Civil Government, and from his *Essay on Human Understanding* on the other. Whenever these are expounded by scholars, the political writings are discussed independently of the *Essay* and the *Essay* independently of the political writings. The reason for this is obviously that scholars have seen very little connexion between Locke's principal works. This has been changed with the appearance of a manuscript in which are preserved eight essays on the law of nature written by Locke in Latin shortly after the Restoration of 1660 and thirty years before the appearance in print of his major works. This manuscript has been published by me, and it is now possible to recognize that Locke's two main bodies of doctrine, namely his political theory and his theory of knowledge, have a common ground and that this lies in his early doctrine of natural law. Admittedly, the notion of a natural law can be seen to be of central importance in his treatise on Civil Government and it also plays its part in the *Essay*. But disappointingly little is said by Locke about this notion in either of these writings, and it is not until the appearance of his essays on natural law that we learn that there is an important relation between the two main parts of his teaching and what this relation is.

In this paper I wish to examine Locke's arguments concerning the existence and binding force of natural law. I have already touched

* Reprinted from *Philosophy*, Vol. 21 (1956), 23–35, by permission of the Editors.

upon certain aspects of this question in the introduction to my edition, but there they were related to their historical setting and other side-issues. Now my purpose is more specific. I am also concluding this paper with an entry in Locke's *Journal*, which contains certain basic ideas of his theory of natural law and which has for some reason or other escaped publication.

The law of nature as it occurs in Locke's philosophy is not the same as one of Galileo's or Newton's so-called laws of nature: it is not concerned with physical phenomena, their motion or regularity. In the sense in which Locke uses the term, it refers to human behaviour and to a moral law. In this sense the notion of a law of nature has had a well-known history among moralists, political theorists, jurists, and theologians before and after Locke's time.

The first perhaps to introduce the idea was Aristotle. He contrasted the uniform behaviour of things in nature with the varieties of human codes of behaviour. Fire, he said, always burns alike no matter where or when it is lit; whether in Greece or in Persia, to-day or a thousand years ago. On the other hand the customs of men, their moral and municipal laws vary from place to place and change from one time to another. However, there is for Aristotle one form of moral law which is eternal and immutable and has the same force everywhere; and because this law is supposed to be as uniform as a law governing natural phenomena he refers to it as a *natural* moral law, sharply distinguishing it from man-made laws which he calls conventional.

This idea of a natural law obtained great influence throughout the period when the Roman Empire spread and the whole of civilized humanity was thought to form one universal community, in which all men were equal by virtue of their common rational nature. The stoic philosophers and the Roman lawyers elaborated this idea and Cicero gave it a famous definition. He speaks of true law as being right reason in agreement with nature, of universal application and unchanging; that there is no need for us to look outside ourselves for an interpreter of it, though God is the author of this law and the judge who enforces it.

That Christianity, filling the vacuum caused by the breakdown of the Roman empire, adopted the belief in a law of nature can be seen from the fact that the idea of natural law appears as a basic conception both in the law-books of the Christian emperor Justinian and in Canon law. Throughout the Middle Ages the ultimate appeal regarding morals, politics, law and also divinity was to natural law, and by natural law the schoolmen meant a law promulgated by God in a natural way and known by reason, i.e. a law other than God's positive law which is known by revelation. Natural law together with the law laid down in the Scriptures was thus regarded as constituting the whole of the divine law. As such it was accepted as an objective 'rule and measure,' an absolute controlling principle.

The fifteenth and sixteenth centuries, as we know, witnessed the emergence of a secular morality, of humanism and the new outlook of the Renaissance. It was in connexion with this new outlook and with the advent of Protestantism which advocated the 'priesthood of all believers' and the necessity of toleration that natural law came to be regarded as a body of individual rights, of subjective claims and thus mainly as a liberating, rather than controlling principle. During the seventeenth and eighteenth centuries the study of natural law was pursued by jurists on the Continent who thought this law to be independent of theological presuppositions and the result of a purely scientific construction, a matter of mathematical deduction. At the same time, while British moralists attempted to provide ethics with a rational foundation, Anglicans sought in the light of contemporary knowledge to redefine the place of natural law within Christian apologetics.

Throughout the nineteenth century, owing to the advance of critical and sceptical arguments, there was a marked tendency to reject many of the traditional criteria of morality and to adopt positivist approaches, particularly in legal theory. In fact, the rise of modern jurisprudence is characterized by the abandonment of the theory of natural law. Also most modern philosophers, analysts as well as positivists, have come to regard this notion as obsolete. Yet we find that between the two wars and again in recent times a number of thinkers have admitted that they cannot dispense with this concept. While admitting this, some would nevertheless maintain that natural law and the theology with which this is associated is pure superstition. For them it is only because the facts involved in law include the *ideas* men have of certain general or supernatural characteristics that the legal philosopher must take them into account. On the other hand, there are contemporary thinkers who genuinely believe in some sort of natural law and make this the basis of their own theories.

It is certainly interesting in this connexion to note that it is only in Russia that no traces of natural-law theory have existed at any time. Though Russia, like the West, has a Christian tradition, it differs from the West in having no humanist tradition. And the idea of a natural law, as I have tried to show, was derived in the first instance from pre-Christian thought, that of Aristotle, the Stoics, and Cicero: it is intimately linked with the humanist belief in the efficacy of man's reason, the freedom of his will, and his moral responsibility.

Having sketched the historical development of the idea of natural law, let us consider what doctrine Locke contributed in his published works. His teaching in the *Second Treatise of Government* can be summarized as follows:

The law of nature is a declaration of God's will and a standard of right and wrong. It is a law that already governs the state of nature, i.e. a pre-social state in which all men are free and equal, and in which they live together in peace. If men make promises to one another in the state of nature, they must consider themselves bound by them, 'for truth and keeping faith belong to men as men, and not as members of society.' It is likewise according to this law and prior to any positive civil laws that each man's private property is determined. Though God has given the earth and all its fruits to men in common, the law of nature sets bounds to what each man is allowed to appropriate and keep for himself. Since within these bounds a person's 'right and conveniency' go together, there can be little room for quarrels about property. Further, for Locke part of God's purpose in creating man was to 'put him under strong obligations of necessity, convenience, and inclination to drive him into society, as well as to fit him with understanding and language to continue and enjoy it.' Throughout man's life in society and under political government, the obligations of the law of nature remain valid, and it is only as they are founded on this law that the municipal laws of countries are just laws. In general, political power for Locke is justified only in so far as it preserves men's natural rights, especially those of life and property. Government is thus limited both by natural law and by men's rights, and these two came to be almost identical for Locke. On the other hand, what man did not possess in the state of nature he cannot resign to the community when he enters it: since he had no arbitrary right in the state of nature to act against the law of nature, i.e. to destroy himself or others, or to take away property which is not his, there should not be any such arbitrary power in society.

It can be seen that the part played by natural law in Locke's political theory is indeed fundamental. It is because he believes this law to be the law of the state of nature, and this state of nature to be not altogether annulled when it is superseded by men's life in society, that for him natural law remains valid in society and in fact sets limits to political government. To put the point less metaphorically: because he is rational, man, according to Locke, is eternally subject to natural law, itself a rational law, regardless of whether or not he lives in an established society.

Unfortunately, despite the basic importance of natural law for Locke's political theory, there is little real discussion of it in any of his mature published writings. In a passage of his *Second Treatise of Government* he even expressly declines an investigation of the particulars of this law; yet what we should like him to tell us particularly is how he thinks we come to know natural law, and how and to what extent it can be said to be binding. In my view, Locke tended in his later years to regard the notion of a law of nature as a mere premise of his thought, as something he believed in but barely investigated. The reason for this attitude, I think, is to be found in difficulties he had in reconciling the notion of this law with some of his mature doctrines. For instance, the development of his hedonistic views and his philosophy of language in the *Essay* had made it difficult for him to attempt a full exposition of natural law or even to believe in it whole-heartedly.

However, with the discovery of Locke's early manuscript on natural law we are in a position to fill in the picture which is left rather vague in his mature works. We can see now that most of his remarks about the law of nature in the *Second Treatise* and the *Essay* have their origin in his early essays. In particular, two crucial questions (about which there is hardly any discussion at all in his mature writings) obviously exercised his mind when he was writing the essays, i.e. the epistemological question—how do we know the law of nature?—and the moral question—how and to what extent is that law binding?

Because of the relatively full account which the essays provide of Locke's views on natural law, it is also possible now to point to definite weaknesses in his theory and to state one's criticisms in precise terms. In a sense it is not surprising to find that the thought of publishing his early work on natural law receded from Locke's mind and that the moral doctrines of his youth were not wholly absorbed in the writings of his maturity. There is a great deal of ambiguity in this notion of a law of nature, and a philosopher naturally feels called upon to disentangle the complex of different issues that it contains.

The concept that has given rise to confusion in theories of natural law is that of reason or rationality, and I propose now to investigate the meaning of this term in so far as it concerns us here.

If asked exactly what commands form part of the law of nature, Locke and most other theorists, I believe, would include the following: to preserve life, to beget and bring up children, to worship God, to obey parents, to show gratitude to benefactors, to respect another's property, and to live in society with other men. Now all these commands have a show of truth or reason and imply duties that would seem to be obvious and readily acceptable to common sense. However, other dictates of this law might not seem to be equally patent, and it has therefore been considered necessary for man, in order that he may know his duties, to employ his mental faculties, i.e. his senses and his understanding. One of the reasons, in fact, why natural law has been called a *natural* law is that the knowledge of it is said to be acquired by man's *natural* faculties, i.e. sense-perception and reason, the joint exercise of which constitutes what Locke and others called the 'light of nature.' The 'light of nature' is thus reason and the law of nature is a law of reason, a law that does not bind children, idiots, or animals, precisely because they are by nature devoid of understanding in the ordinary sense.

To conceive of law as a law of reason has no doubt advantages, particularly that of making it capable of treatment apart from man's emotional nature and thereby securing for it complete impartiality. 'Law,' as Aristotle has said, 'is reason free from all passion and a neutral authority.' But—and here we come to the crucial point—does the conception of law as a law of reason imply that it is possible to justify it rationally, and if so, has any one of the many theorists who throughout the ages have made attempts in this direction been successful?

I am inclined to answer both these questions by saying that a rational defence of natural law is bound to fail because it is liable to involve confused ideas about reason. Issues that should be clearly distinguished from one another in any truly rational exposition are obscured if one passes from statements concerning matters of fact to definitions, thence to statements about ways of knowledge, to judgments of value, and finally to logical truths, assuming throughout that each of the passages is a step in one and the same sort of inferential process, and that each is concerned with one and the same meaning of rationality.

It can be shown, I believe, that a confusion of this kind occurs in every theory of natural law: I can only give one example here, and I will try to show how the confusion arises in Locke's theory. The line of my enquiry will follow what I take to be the logical steps of his argument. They are briefly these: Locke passes from the factual statement that man possesses reason to the conclusion that reason is his essential characteristic and hence to the assumption that reason leads to the discovery of moral truths and, if properly employed, to the discovery of one and the same set of moral truths, i.e. natural law. From this he is led to infer ethical assertions to the effect that the moral standards discovered by reason are themselves rational and that they are commands binding on all men. From this he passes to the belief that the validity of such commands can be proved by reason, and even shown to be necessary in the same way as a geometrical demonstration or a logical deduction.

Locke's starting-point is simple: it is the factual statement that men possess reason and use their reason. The fact that some men cannot reason and that some of those who can do not is admitted by Locke, and he refers to idiots and children and to those who because of their emotional nature or because they are lazy or careless, make no proper use of their reason. In spite of this admission, his next step is to assert that men not only can reason but that reason is their defining property and that therefore their special function is to exercise it, i.e. that they are obliged to use their reason.

Locke's inference here is from the matter-of-fact proposition—if it is matter-of-fact proposition—that all men are rational, to the statement—which is a definition—that in order to be truly men, men must be rational. This statement is not so much about an indisputable fact as a belief derived from Aristotle's idea of 'fixed natures.' Though definitions depend in some sense on evidence, they are not empirical statements, i.e. statements about fact, which can be either true or false; hence definitions cannot be validated or invalidated by statements of a purely factual kind. Moreover, from a statement about man's defining characteristic, i.e. a statement that is neither a moral one nor a necessary one, the *moral* proposition is inferred that he has a duty to live in conformity with his essential nature. This conformity is in its turn twofold: it may mean that it is man's duty to use reason and also that he has a duty to obey reason, i.e. to accept the findings of reason. Further, it is implied in Locke's whole argument that the very question at issue, namely whether reason is an essential characteristic of men and whether they are therefore obliged to use it is decided affirmatively by reason itself. I conclude then that we are here confronted with various meanings of the term reason which Locke does not disentangle, and also with statements of different kinds so that it is not always possible to pass from one to the other and to apply to each the same sort of proof.

Let us now consider Locke's answer to the question how men come to know natural law.

Obviously, in connexion with this question, reason will have to be discussed on two levels: firstly, as a mental 'activity' of man leading to the production or discovery of moral truth; secondly, as the spiritual product of this activity, consisting of a body of rational principles or rules of conduct. Locke is careful to distinguish between the two meanings of reason. By the first he understands the discursive faculty of the mind which seeks to discover truth by forming arguments from things known to things unknown. By the second he understands a set of moral truths which can become an object of knowledge and a rule of action, and this he calls 'right reason.' Whereas for him the discursive faculty like the organs of sense is inborn in man, 'right reason' is not. And for him also, the moral truths coming before the mind are not made or dictated by human reason, but merely discovered and interpreted by it. Thus in a way he still regards human reason as a sort of cause of which truth is the effect: it does not bring truth into existence but it leads to its knowledge. I will not raise here the question whether reason can be regarded as a cause rather than simply as a way of doing or considering something; nor will I examine whether rules of conduct are discovered rather than made, as the study of anthropology would suggest. I think however that Locke's belief in the causal efficacy of reason was a half-hearted one since according to him reason cannot be regarded as a *source* of knowledge. By itself, he would say, reason provides no primary notions and it therefore requires some material which can serve as a starting-point for its operations. According to him the material in question is provided by sense-perception.

It is here, in connexion with his early theory of natural law that Locke's empiricism, his well-known emphasis on knowledge by the senses, has its origin. For this reason I said at the beginning of my paper that Locke's two main bodies of doctrine, namely his theory of knowledge and his political philosophy, have a common ground and that this lies in his early doctrine of natural law.

The steps whereby in Locke's view reason leads to the knowledge of natural law from such data as the senses supply are briefly these:

Our senses tell us not only of bodies and their motions but also of beauty and regularity in all parts of the world. Since this beauty and regularity must be the result of some superior design, reason infers the existence of a most wise and powerful Creator. This argument from design together with the so-called anthropological argument are singled out by Locke from among the traditional proofs of God's existence precisely because these two arguments are derived from sense-experience and, apart from rational inference, require no further support, whereas all other such proofs presuppose *a priori* notions which Locke is unwilling to accept. Locke goes on to show that since God is not only powerful but also wise, He has designed the world for some purpose and that we find in everything a definite rule or pattern appropriate to its nature. God's purpose in creating man was that he should live according to reason. Two particular functions he is intended to perform are to worship God and to live in society with other men.

What Locke has endeavoured to establish so far is firstly that there exists a law-maker, i.e. some superior power to which man is rightly subject, and secondly that this law-maker has expressed a will, this being the law of nature. Thus in Locke's view it is reason in co-operation with sense-experience which reveals the existence of a natural law and also the dictates of this law. The whole of Locke's argument here is derived from the scholastics and there is nothing original about it except perhaps his insistence on the part played by sense-perception. Whether novel or not, one may wonder if the argument forms the right approach to the question at issue. When asking himself whether natural law can be known, Locke does not for a moment consider the possibility that this law, and expressions of value generally, might not belong to the class of things of which it makes sense to say that they are known in the ordinary sense of the word, i.e. that statements about them can be justified by reference to empirical facts, to rules of inference, or to self-evident truths. Locke does not face this issue and instead makes the *proper employment* of man's natural faculties a necessary and sufficient condition for the knowledge of natural law. Yet no matter to what extent men's senses and their reason are found to be efficient, this efficiency is no criterion by which to decide whether natural law is a proper object of knowledge. Such a decision must be derived from an analysis of the concept of natural law rather different from the one Locke offered.

The next step in Locke's argument again consists of an inference: he passes from what he has hitherto established to ethical assertions concerning the binding force of natural law. Having shown that man's reason can lead to the discovery of certain rational principles, he goes on to conclude that man is morally obliged to accept these findings of his reason. In other words, Locke starts with certain statements of *fact*, i.e. statements about human nature, containing no judgments of value; he then passes to certain metaphysical and theological statements which contain no moral words either; from these statements he draws a conclusion about what men *ought to do*, as if the conclusion of a valid argument could contain anything, e.g. an '*ought*,' which is not contained in the premises. The point that it is impossible to deduce an ethical conclusion from premises that are non-ethical was made forcibly by Hume in a celebrated passage. 'In every system of morality,' he says, '. . . I have always remarked, that the author proceeds for some time in the ordinary way of reasoning, and establishes the being of a God, or makes observations concerning human affairs; when of a sudden I am surprised to find, that instead of the usual copulations of propositions, *is,* and *is not,* I meet with no proposition that is not connected with an *ought,* or an *ought not.* . . . As this *ought,* or *ought not* expresses some new relation or affirmation, it is necessary that it should be explained; and at the same time that a reason should be given . . . how this new relation can be a deduction from others, which are entirely different from it.' Hume concludes from these observations that they would 'subvert all the vulgar systems of morality, and let us see, that the distinction of vice and virtue is not . . . perceived by reason.'

Let us consider briefly at which point in Locke's argument moral assertions are introduced. They appear in two contexts. One is where Locke advances his proof of God's existence and the 'voluntarist' theory (or rather definition) that law or men's duties are the expression of a superior will. For Locke then moral obligations are binding because they arise from God's commands. Now from saying that God commands us to do certain actions we cannot infer that we ought to do them, not even if we add the further premise that God commands us to obey His commands. The ethical statement concerning our duty to do certain actions can be derived only from another ethical statement such as that we ought to do what God commands. For Locke such a derivation is in fact possible since he argues that obedience to God's will is right, that is, obligatory. However any deduction from this premise or first moral principle, i.e. that a creature ought to obey the wish of his Creator, may be said to be compelling only if the premise is self-evident, which is doubtful in Locke's example, for it would not be self-contradictory to reject the principle that obedience to God's will is right. Moreover, the 'voluntarist' theory carries with it an implication which Locke obviously found dissatisfying, for together with the concept of will it introduces an arbitrary element into morality.

In order to make his theory more perfect, Locke attempts to derive moral obligation in some other way. He does this as part of his endeavour to arrive at a purely rational foundation of ethics. For him human reason not only indicates or teaches what man's duties are, but at the same time makes his duties binding; it is thus a self-depending source of obligation. He maintains that natural law is coeval with the human race and that all men are subject to it since it is 'so firmly rooted in the soil of human nature.' In his view there is in fact a 'harmony' or 'conformity' (*convenientia*) between moral values and man's rational nature; for as man's nature is always the same so reason 'pronounces' a fixed and permanent rule of morals. One may wonder how from these views Locke can arrive at a theory of moral obligation. To derive natural law from man's rational nature, and this, in its turn, from God's wisdom in creating man such that certain duties follow from his constitution is to draw an ethical conclusion from entirely non-ethical premises. Therefore the same objection applies here as in connexion with the 'voluntarist' theory of law. To put the point differently one might say that reason can perhaps declare what type of action is in accordance with man's nature and is therefore in *some* sense necessary; but it does not thereby prove a moral obligation to perform the action. Grotius, Locke's contemporary, admitted that natural law, if defined as a dictate of right reason only *indicates* whether or not an action is morally necessary, and before him Suarez had pointed out that in this capacity it would be of the nature of a *directive* rule rather than of a law in the strict sense, a law having a binding force.

But this difficulty, Locke would argue, can be overcome by establishing a close analogy between moral knowledge and mathematics. The step he proposes now is a further example of a doubtful, if not illegitimate, passage from one kind of discourse to another. For from assertions about moral rules he passes to the assertion that the validity of these rules can be proved, and even shown to be necessary in the same way as a geometrical demonstration.

Locke advances his new argument in connexion with his notion of a harmony between natural law and man's rational nature. Thus he says: 'In fact it seems to me to follow just as necessarily from the nature of man that, if he is a man, he is bound to love and worship God and also to fulfil other things appropriate to the rational nature, i.e. to observe the law of nature, as it follows from the nature of a triangle that, if it is a triangle, its three angles are equal to two right angles.' By analogy with mathematical necessity Locke here endeavours to establish the *necessary* validity of moral rules. It is not altogether clear, however, whether in this passage he thinks of moral truths as self-evident principles or as deductions from self-evident principles. From another passage where he wants to make clear that man's duties necessarily follow from his very nature it might appear that he regards moral truths as self-evident; for he compares the way in which these are apprehended to the way in which men, so long as they can see and the sun shines, must of necessity come to know the alternations of day and night and the differences between colours and between a curved and a straight line. The point he seems anxious to make in both passages is that from the concept of man's nature, *if suitably defined*, propositions concerning moral obligation would follow either analytically or by the rules of deductive inference, just as in mathematics, granting certain definitions, we accept some propositions as self-evident and others as demonstrable.

Here, in the setting of his early doctrine of natural law, we meet with the first example of Locke's celebrated contention that mathematics and morality are parallel in that they both contain self-evident truths and are capable of demonstration. Several of his contemporaries, e.g. Grotius, and also certain British moralists following him, e.g. Samuel Clarke, held a similar view. They found this view attractive for two reasons: firstly, it presented an improvement on a legislative ethics which they regarded as unsatisfactory because of the element of arbitrariness it contains; secondly, the view of the demonstrability of ethics seemed to them to allow moral rules to be regarded as independent of a superior will and at the same time as necessarily valid, i.e. not merely directive but binding. Whatever advantages Locke may have hoped to derive from this view, it raises difficulties for his argument in the essays.

There are two alternatives to be considered. On the one hand, Locke may have been tempted to accept moral *definitions* as the starting-point of a demonstrative deduction of ethics; he did so, for instance, in his mature work, the *Essay* (IV. III. 18), where he derives the proposition that 'where there is no property there is no injustice' from preliminary definitions of property as a right to anything and of injustice as the violation of that right. Here he is confronted with the same problem as in the case of someone trying to draw an ethical conclusion from non-ethical premises; for to deduce an ethical proposition from definitions should be just as impossible. On the other hand, if Locke accepts *self-evident* moral truths as the first principles of his demonstrative science of ethics the only justification he has for this is his belief in the analogy between moral knowledge and mathematics, or vision respectively. It is far from obvious, however, that such a parallel can be accepted. All that Locke has shown is that there are self-evident principles in mathematics and that certain empirical propositions can in some sense be called self-evident. Without a demonstration of the truth of the analogy on which he relies he cannot claim to have indicated the existence of self-evident *moral* propositions, or, for that matter, of a demonstrative science of ethics. In fact, moral ideas and judgments are very different from those of mathematics, and moral obligation is a kind of necessity that differs from logical necessity as it does from causal necessity. In other words, any attempt to prove that a moral rule is binding is doomed to fail if it is considered to be the same as an attempt to prove that a geometrical demonstration is valid.

I conclude that, for the reasons I have given, Locke's theory of natural law is open to criticism; that because the difficulties which beset his theory are liable to be present in any philosophical defence of this law as a law of reason, no such defence can ever succeed. To say this is not to deny that natural law is acceptable as the basis of moral obligation if one regards it as a premise of thought which cannot be further justified by reason, i.e. as an article of faith, or an ideal. But this would be a very different issue from that which I have discussed in this paper, and because it is not primarily a philosophical problem, I do not propose to go into it further. It should be remembered, however, that Locke himself, in his later years, came to regard the idea of a law of nature as a mere premise of his thought, and that he must have perceived certain theoretical difficulties in this notion, for he could never bring himself to publish his own doctrine in the essays.

Here then is a summary of what I have tried to say in this paper. First I outlined the development of the idea of natural law from antiquity to modern times. Then I gave a brief account of what Locke says about natural law in his *Treatise of Government* and showed that as a rational law it is of fundamental importance for his political and moral philosophy. However, we find the most detailed account of his doctrine of natural law in recently discovered essays, the work of his youth, and it is because there he enters so fully into the particulars of this law that it is possible for us to subject his theory to a close examination and to point out exactly where the weaknesses lie. We saw that the chief difficulty arises from an ambiguity in the central notion, that of reason. I explained that this ambiguity is liable to give rise to confusions in any theory of natural law to the extent that such a theory represents an attempt to justify rationally the moral law as a law of reason. Such a process of justification would be in the form of a logical deduction; but since the main term, that of reason, would be employed in different senses, there are bound to occur illegitimate inferences from one *kind* of discourse to another. The inferences in Locke's argument are from factual statements concerning reason to definitions concerning reason; thence to statements about discoveries made by reason, from which certain ethical statements concerning the binding force of rational principles are derived; these statements, in their turn, are thought to be like statements in mathematics, i.e. capable of logical proof, an analogy which obscures the distinction between moral and logical necessity.

[The following is Locke's *Journal* entry for 15 July, 1678 (Bodleian MS. Locke f.3, pp. 201–2), headed *Lex naturae*. The chronological context in which it falls is discussed in my edition of Locke's essays on natural law, pp. 66–7; the moral doctrine of which it forms a part is to my mind best explained by H. Sidgwick in his *Outlines of the History of Ethics*, 6th ed., 1946, pp. 175–8. I have modernized the spelling and punctuation of the passage, published here for the first time.

'God having given man *above other creatures of this habitable part of the universe* a knowledge of himself which the beasts have not, he is thereby under obligations, which the beasts are not, for knowing God to be a wise agent; he cannot but conclude that he has that knowledge and those faculties which he finds in himself above the other creatures given him for some use and end. If therefore he comprehends the relation between father and son and finds it reasonable that his son whom he has begot (only in pursuance of his pleasure without thinking of his son) and nourished should obey, love, and reverence him and be grateful to him, he cannot but find it much more reasonable that he and every other man should obey and revere, love and thank the author of their being to whom they owe all that they are. If he finds it reasonable to punish one of his children that injures another, he cannot but expect the same from God the Father of all men, when any one injures another; if he finds it reasonable that his children should assist and help one another and expects it from them as their duty, will he not also by the same reason conclude that God expects the same of all men one to another? If he finds that God has made him and all other men in a state wherein they cannot subsist without society and has given them judgement to discern what is capable of preserving that society, can he but conclude that he is obliged and that God requires him to follow those rules which conduce to the preserving of society?']

LOCKE AND THE MODERN THEORY OF NATURAL RIGHT*

Leo Strauss

What is the reason why, according to Locke, the admission of a law of nature requires the admission of a state of nature, and more particularly the admission that in the state of nature "every man hath the right to . . . be executioner of the law of nature"? ". . . Since it would be utterly in vain to suppose a rule set to the free actions of man, without annexing to it some enforcement of good or evil to determine his will, we must wherever we suppose a law, suppose also some reward or punishment annexed to that law." In order to be a law, the law of nature must have sanctions. According to the traditional view those sanctions are supplied by the judgment of the conscience, which is the judgment of God. Locke rejects this view. According to him, the judgment of the conscience is so far from being the judgment of God that the conscience "is nothing else but our own opinion or judgment of the moral rectitude or pravity of our own actions." Or to quote Hobbes, whom Locke tacitly follows: "private consciences . . . are but private opinions." Conscience cannot therefore be a guide; still less can it supply sanctions. Or if the verdict of the conscience is identified with right opinion about the moral quality of our actions, it is utterly powerless by itself: "View but an army at the sacking of a town, and see what observation or sense of moral principles, or what touch of conscience, for all the outrages they do." If there are to be sanctions for the law of nature in this world, those sanctions must be applied by human beings. But any "enforcement" of the law of nature which takes place in and through civil society appears to be the outcome of human convention. Therefore, the law of nature will not be effective in this world and hence not be a true law, if it is not effective in the state antedating civil society or government—in the state of

* Reprinted from *Natural Right and History* (Chicago, 1953), pp. 222–230, by permission of the University of Chicago Press and the author. Some of the notes have been slightly altered. Copyright 1953 by The University of Chicago.

nature; even in the state of nature everyone must be effectively responsible to other human beings. This, however, requires that everyone in the state of nature have the right to be the executioner of the law of nature: "the law of nature would, as all other laws that concern men in this world, be in vain, if there were nobody that in the state of nature had a power to execute that law." The law of nature is indeed given by God, but its being a law does not require that it be known to be given by God, because it is immediately enforced, not by God or by the conscience, but by human beings.[1]

The law of nature cannot be truly a law if it is not effective in the state of nature. It cannot be effective in the state of nature if the state of nature is not a state of peace. The law of nature imposes on everyone the perfect duty of preserving the rest of mankind "as much as he can," but only "when his own preservation comes not in competition." If the state of nature were characterized by habitual conflict between self-preservation and the preservation of others, the law of nature which "willeth the peace and preservation of all mankind" would be ineffectual: the higher claim of self-preservation would leave no room for concern with others. The state of nature must therefore be "a state of peace, good-will, mutual assistance, and preservation." This means that the state of nature must be a social state; in the state of nature all men "make up one society" by virtue of the law of nature, although they have no "common superior on earth." Inasmuch as self-preservation requires food and other necessities, and scarcity of such

---

[1] Locke, *The Reasonableness of Christianity* (in *The Works of John Locke in Nine Volumes* VI [London, 1824]), 114: ". . . if there were no punishment for the transgressors of [Jesus' laws], his laws would not be the laws of a king, . . . but empty talk, without force, and without influence." *Two Treatises*, II, secs. 7, 8, 13 end, 21 end; cf. *ibid.*, sec. 11, with I, sec. 56. *Essay concerning human understanding*, I, 3, secs. 6–9, and II, 28, sec. 6; Thomas Hobbes, *Leviathan*, ed. Michael Oakeshott, chap. xxix (212). When speaking of everyone's natural right to be the executioner of the law of nature, Locke refers to "that great law of nature, 'Whoso sheddeth man's blood, by man shall his blood be shed' " (Gen. 9:6). But he omits the biblical reason, "for in the image of God made he man." The Lockean reason for the right to inflict capital punishment on murderers is that man may "destroy *things* noxious" to men (the italics are not in the original). Locke disregards the fact that both the murdered and the murderer are made in the image of God: the murderer "may be destroyed as a lion or a tiger, one of those wild savage beasts with whom men can have no society nor security" (*Treatises*, II, sects. 8, 10, 11, 16, 172, 181; cf. I, sec. 30). Cf. Thomas Aquinas *Summa theologica* i. qu. 79, *a.* 13 and ii. 1. qu. 96, *a.* 5 ad 3 (cf. *a.* 4, obj. 1); Richard Hooker, *Laws of Ecclesiastical Polity*, I, 9, sec. 2–10, sec. 1; Hugo Grotuis, *De jure belli ac Pacis*, Prolegomena, secs. 20 and 27; Richard Cumberland, *De legibus naturae*, chap. I, sec. 26.

things leads to conflict, the state of nature must be a state of plenty: "God has given us all things richly." The law of nature cannot be a law if it is not known; it must be known and therefore it must be knowable in the state of nature.[2]

After having drawn or suggested this picture of the state of nature especially in the first pages of the *Treatise*, Locke demolishes it as his argument proceeds. The state of nature, which at first glance seems to be the golden age ruled by God or good demons, is literally a state without government, "pure anarchy." It could last forever, "were it not for the corruption and viciousness of degenerate men"; but unfortunately "the greater part" are "no strict observers of equity and justice." For this reason, to say nothing of others, the state of nature has great "inconveniences." Many "mutual grievances, injuries and wrongs . . . attend men in the state of nature"; "strife and troubles would be endless" in it. It "is full of fears and continual dangers." It is "in ill condition." Far from being a state of peace, it is a state in which peace and quiet are uncertain. The state of peace is civil society; the state antedating civil society is the state of war.[3] This is either the cause or the effect of the fact that the state of nature is a state not of plenty but of penury. Those living in it are "needy and wretched." Plenty requires civil society.[4] Being "pure anarchy," the state of nature is not likely to be a social state. In fact, it is characterized by "want of society." "Society" and "civil society" are synonymous terms. The state of nature is "loose." For "the first and strongest desire God planted in man" is not the concern with others, not even concern with one's offspring, but the desire for self-preservation.[5]

The state of nature would be a state of peace and good will if men in the state of nature were under the law of nature. But "nobody can be under a law which is not promulgated to him." Man would know the law of nature in the state of nature if "the dictates of the law of nature" were "implanted in him" or "writ in the hearts of mankind." But no moral rules are "imprinted in our minds" or "written on [our] hearts" or "stamped upon [our] minds" or "implanted." Since there is no *habitus* of moral principles, no *synderesis* or conscience, all

[2] *Treatises*, I, sec. 43; II, secs. 6, 7, 11, 19, 28, 31, 51, 56–57, 110, 128, 171, 172.
[3] *Ibid.*, II, secs. 13, 74, 90, 91 and note, 94, 105, 123, 127, 128, 131, 135n., 136, 212, 225–27.
[4] *Ibid.*, secs. 32, 37, 38, 41–43, 49.
[5] *Ibid.*, secs. 21, 74, 101, 105, 116, 127, 131 beginning, 132 beginning, 134 beginning (cf. 124 beginning), 211, 220, 243; cf. I, sec. 56, with sec. 88. Cf. both passages, as well as I, sec. 97, and II, secs. 60, 63, 67, 170, with *Essay*, I, 3, secs. 3, 9, 19.

knowledge of the law of nature is acquired by study: to know the law of nature, one must be "a studier of that law." The law of nature becomes known only through demonstration. The question, therefore, is whether men in the state of nature are capable of becoming studiers of the law of nature. "The greatest part of mankind want leisure or capacity for demonstration. . . . And you may as soon hope to have all the day-labourers and tradesmen, and spinsters and dairy-maids, perfect mathematicians, as to have them perfect in ethics this way." Yet a day laborer in England is better off than a king of the Americans, and "in the beginning all the world was America, and more so than it is now." "The first ages" are characterized by "negligent and unforeseeing innocence" rather than by habits of study.[6] The condition in which man lives in the state of nature—"continual dangers" and "penury"—make impossible knowledge of the law of nature: the law of nature is not promulgated in the state of nature. Since the law of nature must be promulgated in the state of nature if it is to be a law in the proper sense of the term, we are again forced to conclude that the law of nature is not a law in the proper sense of the term.[7]

What, then, is the status of the law of nature in Locke's doctrine? What is its foundation? There is no rule of the law of nature which is innate, "that is, . . . imprinted on the mind as a duty." This is shown by the fact that there are no rules of the law of nature, "which, as practical principles ought, do continue constantly to operate and influence all our actions without ceasing [and which] may be observed in all persons and all ages, steady and universal." However, "Nature . . . has put into man a desire of happiness, and an aversion to misery; these, indeed, are innate practical principles": they are universally and unceasingly effective. The desire for happiness and the pursuit of happiness to which it gives rise are not duties. But "men . . . must be allowed to pursue their happiness, nay, cannot be hindered." The desire for happiness and the pursuit of happiness have the character of an absolute right, of a natural right. There is, then, an innate natural right, while there is no innate natural duty. To understand how this is possible, one merely has to reformulate our last quotation: pursuit of happiness is a right, it "must be allowed," because "it cannot be hindered." It is a right antedating all duties for the same reason that,

---

[6] Cf., above all, *Treatises*, II, secs. 11 end, and 56, with *Essay*, I, 3, sec. 8, and I, 4, sec. 12; *Treatises*, II, secs. 6, 12, 41, 49, 57, 94, 107, 124, 136; *Essay*, I, 3, secs. 1, 6, 9, 11–13, 26, 27; *Reasonableness*, pp. 146, 139, 140. Cf. n. 74 above.

[7] Cf. the use of the term "crime" (as distinguished from "sin") in *Treatises*, II, secs. 10, 11, 87, 128, 218, 230, with *Essay*, II, 28, secs. 7–9.

according to Hobbes, establishes as the fundamental moral fact the right of self-preservation: man must be allowed to defend his life against violent death because he is driven to do so by some natural necessity which is not less than that by which a stone is carried downward. Being universally effective, natural right, as distinguished from natural duty, is effective in the state of nature: man in the state of nature is "absolute lord of his own person and possessions."[8] Since the right of nature is innate, whereas the law of nature is not, the right of nature is more fundamental than the law of nature and is the foundation of the law of nature.

Since happiness presupposes life, the desire for life takes precedence over the desire for happiness in case of conflict. This dictate of reason is at the same time a natural necessity: "the first and strongest desire God planted in men, and wrought into the very principles of their nature, is that of self-preservation." The most fundamental of all rights is therefore the right of self-preservation. While nature has put into man "a strong desire of preserving his life and being," it is only man's reason which teaches him what is "necessary and useful to his being." And reason—or, rather, reason applied to a subject to be specified presently—is the law of nature. Reason teaches that "he that is master of himself and his own life has a right, too, to the means of preserving it." Reason further teaches that, since all men are equal in regard to the desire, and hence to the right, of self-preservation, they are equal in the decisive respect, notwithstanding any natural inequalities in other respects.[9] From this Locke concludes, just as Hobbes did, that in the state of nature everyone is the judge of what means are conducive to his self-preservation, and this leads him, as it did Hobbes, to the further conclusion that in the state of nature "any man may do what he thinks fit."[10] No wonder, therefore, that the state of nature is "full of fears and continual dangers." But reason teaches that life cannot be preserved, let alone enjoyed, except in a state of peace: reason wills peace. Reason therefore wills such courses of action as are

[8] *Essay*, I, 3, secs. 3 and 12; *Reasonableness*, p. 148; *Treatises*, II, sec. 123 (cf. sec. 6). Cf. Hobbes, *De cive*, I, 7, and III, 27n.

[9] *Treatises*, I, secs. 86–88, 90 beginning, 111 toward the end; II, secs. 6, 54, 149, 168, 172. One may describe the relation of the right of self-preservation to the right to the pursuit of happiness as follows: the former is the right to "subsist" and implies the right to what is necessary to man's being; the second is the right to "enjoy the conveniences of life" or to "comfortable preservation" and implies, therefore, also the right to what is useful to man's being without being necessary for it (cf. *Treatises*, I, secs. 86, 87, 97; II, secs. 26, 34, 41).

[10] *Ibid.*, II, secs. 10, 13, 87, 94, 105, 129, 168, 171.

conducive to peace. Reason dictates, accordingly, that "no one ought to harm another," that he who harms another—who therefore has renounced reason—may be punished by everyone and that he who is harmed may take reparations. These are the fundamental rules of the law of nature on which the argument of the *Treatise* is based: the law of nature is nothing other than the sum of the dictates of reason in regard to men's "mutual security" or to "the peace and safety" of mankind. Since in the state of nature all men are judges in their own cases and since, therefore, the state of nature is characterized by constant conflict that arises from the very law of nature, the state of nature is "not to be endured": the only remedy is government or civil society. Reason accordingly dictates how civil society must be constructed and what its rights or bounds are: there is a rational public law or a natural constitutional law. The principle of that public law is that all social or governmental power is derivative from powers which by nature belong to the individuals. The contract of the individuals actually concerned with their self-preservation—not the contract of the fathers qua fathers or divine appointment or an end of man that is independent of the actual wills of all individuals—creates the whole power of society: "the supreme power in every commonwealth [is] but the joint power of every member of the society."[11]

Locke's natural law teaching can then be understood perfectly if one assumes that the laws of nature which he admits are, as Hobbes put it, "but conclusions, or theorems concerning what conduces to the conservation and defense" of man over against other men. And it must be thus understood, since the alternative view is exposed to the difficulties which have been set forth. The law of nature, as Locke conceives of it, formulates the conditions of peace or, more generally stated, of "public happiness" or "the prosperity of any people." There is therefore a kind of sanction for the law of nature in this world: the disregard of the law of nature leads to public misery and penury. But this sanction is insufficient. Universal compliance with the law of nature would indeed guarantee perpetual peace and prosperity everywhere on earth. Failing such universal compliance, however, it may well happen that a society which complies with the law of nature enjoys less of temporal happiness than a society which transgresses the law of nature. For in both foreign and domestic affairs victory does not always favor "the right side": the "great robbers . . . are too big for the weak hands of justice in this world." There remains, however,

---

[11] *Ibid.*, secs. 4, 6–11, 13, 96, 99, 127–30, 134, 135, 142, 159.

at least this difference between those who strictly comply with the law of nature and those who do not, that only the former can act and speak consistently; only the former can consistently maintain that there is a fundamental difference between civil societies and gangs of robbers, a distinction to which every society and every government is forced to appeal time and again. In a word, the law of nature is "a creature of the understanding rather than a work of nature"; it is "barely in the mind," a "notion," and not "in the things themselves." This is the ultimate reason why ethics can be raised to the rank of a demonstrative science.[12]

[12] *Ibid.*, secs. 1, 12, 176–77, 202; *Essay*, III, 5, sec. 12, and IV, 12, secs. 7–9 (cf. Spinoza, *Ethics*, IV, praef. and 18 schol.). As for the element of legal fiction invoved in "the law of nature and reason," cf. *Treatises*, II, sec. 98 beginning, with sec. 96. Cf. *Reasonableness*, p. 11: "the law of reason, or, as it is called, the law of nature." Cf. also Hobbes, *De cive*, Ep. ded., and *Leviathan*, chap. xv (96 and 104–5).

LOCKE AND HIS INTERPRETERS*

Charles H. Monson, Jr.

✧

One of the more interesting phenomena of recent philosophical scholarship has been the interest shown in John Locke. More than a dozen major works have appeared during the past twenty-five years and the spate of articles, on all aspects of his thought, increases every year. But, coincidentally there has been a reassessment of the applicability of traditional democratic principles to a complex industrialized society; hence much of the interest in Locke, understandably, has centred on his political theory.

But some writers, when they return to Locke, have failed to find the natural rights, natural law, contract theory of the state so apparent to their eighteenth-century counterparts. Rather, they have found a theory they describe, variously, as advocating egoism, absolute subordination to majority rule, capitalism, anarchy, the denial of natural law, Hobbesianism, or the absence of natural rights. These writers, careful scholars and systematic thinkers all, challenge the traditional interpretation of Locke, and in a larger sense, the traditional justification for democratic government. Hence, a careful scrutiny of their reports on Locke's real, but as yet misunderstood, political theory seems to be in order.

I

The most recent, the most scholarly, and the most defensible of the 'non-traditional' interpretations is in Leo Strauss's *Natural Right and History*. For purposes of analysis, his account can be reduced to three assertions: first, Locke is not a natural law theorist; second, he is a Hobbesian; and third, his egoism is also demonstrated by his account of property rights.

Strauss argues that Locke cannot be a natural law theorist, for he

* Reprinted from *Political Studies*, Vol. 6 (1958), 120–135, by permission of the Clarendon Press, Oxford.

gives no account of how men know the law of nature. He could have said either reason or revelation, but there are no philosophical theories in the *Second Treatise*[1] and his other works provide no definite answers either. Moreover, the first alternative is unacceptable because rational knowledge also requires proof of God's existence and human immortality, proofs which Locke says are not demonstrable, hence 'natural reason is unable to know the law of nature as a law.'[2] At best, he accepted a 'partial' law of nature, moral rules which correspond to Scriptural injunctions, but his rules, when analysed, are not identical with those of Jesus. Hence, Locke does not adequately account for man's knowledge of natural law and this shows that he 'cannot have recognized any law of nature in the proper sense of the term.'[3]

In the last analysis this argument asserts that you can tell *what* one knows only if he tells you *how* he obtained his knowledge; an interesting, if dubious, assumption which Strauss makes no effort to justify even though his whole argument rests on its validity. But, no matter; grant the assumption and, moreover, grant that Locke did not provide an adequate explanation, still it does not follow that he was not aware of the problem. In the *Second Treatise* he explicitly asks himself how the law of nature can be known and he answers:

> Yet, it is certain there is such a law and that, too, as intelligible and plain to a rational creature and a studier of that law as the positive laws of commonwealth; nay, possibly plainer, as much as reason is easier to be understood than the fancy and intricate contrivances of man.

And again: the law of nature can be understood by men 'who will but consult reason'. Or again: by men 'who will not renounce reason.' And still again: by men 'who live according to reason'.[4] Locke, then, did provide an explanation and his answer makes Strauss's extended criticisms of knowledge by revelation both irrelevant and misleading.

But Strauss, a careful scholar, no doubt was aware of the many places in which Locke says that natural law can be known by reason. Why, then, did he reject these explicit statements? The answer seems to be: they are not enough. We must know more about reason's competence and in *The Reasonableness of Christianity* Locke says that

---

[1] Leo Strauss, *Natural Right and History*, University of Chicago Press, 1953, p. 220. A condensed version appeared in the *Philosophical Review*, October 1952.

[2] Ibid., pp. 203–4.

[3] Ibid., p. 220.

[4] *Second Treatise on Civil Government*, Appleton Century edn., 1937, secs. 12, 6, 11, 19. See also secs. 30, 32, 56, 57, 63. &c.

reason cannot prove God's existence. Therefore, Strauss's argument seems to be: reason cannot know of God's existence, and natural law comes from God, so reason cannot know natural law, and Locke cannot have meant what he said.

This method of argument requires several comments. First, Strauss goes outside the *Treatise* because he is convinced that it contains no philosophical theories, only 'civil' ones; a highly debatable point which, again, he makes no attempt to justify. Second, his choice of the *Reasonableness* as the main source for defining reason's competence is unfortunate, for the work is not primarily concerned with this problem (as was the *Essay*, for instance) and it was a product of Locke's later life, a time when he was more interested in religion than political theory. But, most important, it does not reflect the position Locke takes in the *Treatise*, for there he asserts, more than twenty times, that reason can know natural law. Yet not once does he suggest that one must prove God's existence in order to have this knowledge.

Locke himself points backwards, not forwards, from the *Treatise* for the fuller explanation. He does not say that he will examine the subject more carefully at some future time; rather, he quotes from Hooker and other natural law writers and he suggests, in both the *Treatise* and the early *Essays*, that they have dealt with the subject more or less satisfactorily. If the *Treatise* lacks philosophical cogency, this results from unstated assumptions rather than undeveloped omissions, for Locke believed that when God created man, He gave him the means, natural law and natural reason, as guides and, if man 'will but use his reason, he will know [the law of nature] which directs a free and intelligent agent to his proper interest'.[5]

Strauss contends that Locke is really a Hobbesian because he recognizes no normative law of nature and, on the contrary, frequently asserts egoism and selfishness as men's primary motivation. In the *Essay* Locke says: 'Nature has put into man a desire for happiness, and an aversion to misery; these are, indeed, innate practical principles.' Or, as Strauss restates it: 'The desire for happiness and the pursuit of happiness have the character of an absolute right, a natural right.' This 'right of nature is more fundamental than the law of nature' and since each person is interested in his own happiness, 'the most fundamental of all rights is the right of self-preservation.' Hence, 'Locke's theory can be understood perfectly, if one assumes that the

---

[5] *Treatise*, sec. 57. For a further analysis, see Locke's recently published *Essays on The Law of Nature*, Oxford University Press, 1954.

laws of nature are, as Hobbes put it, "but conclusions or theorems concerning what conduces to the conservation and defence" of man over against other men.'[6]

This line of argument raises no question of scholarship, for Locke does make such statements; the important question is whether these statements are of central importance. Here again we must note Strauss's impatience with the *Treatise,* for he prefers other statements, this time principally from the *Essay,* as the true indicators of Locke's political theory.[7] The procedure, of course, is all right *if* the same information could not be obtained from the *Treatise.* But this claim cannot be supported, for, as Strauss himself recognizes, the *Treatise* contains many descriptive ethical statements.[8]

However, all of them do not stress egoism. Some do, for instance: 'the sacred and unalterable law of self-preservation'; 'the individual's unalterable right to preserve his own property'; and his obligation to help others 'only when his own preservation comes not in competition.'[9] But others do not, for instance: each individual agrees to establish a government where 'the legislative will make laws as the public good of the society shall require', and he obeys a government only when it 'rules for the public good of the people'.[10] From a strictly textual analysis, then, Locke does not have a consistent descriptive theory and it might have been this very inconsistency which drove Strauss to conclude that the fundamental premiss is outside the Treatise.

But the evidence also indicates another conclusion, one closer to Locke's own teaching. Every person *should* follow 'the law of nature which willeth the peace and preservation of all mankind' and some men do what they should while others, indeed, 'the greater portion of mankind', do not.[11] Thus, descriptively some men are egoists, others are not, and Locke's account of human motivation is accurate, although inconsistent. But, in a more important sense, normatively, none should be merely egoists, for each has a natural obligation to preserve others, and a state can exist only if its legislators follow 'that eternal

---

[6] Strauss, op. cit., pp. 226, 227, 229.

[7] But even this hedonism is but a part of the more complex (and confusing) ethical theory of this work. See Sterling Lamprecht, *The Moral and Political Philosophy of John Locke.*

[8] See Strauss, pp. 227–30.

[9] *Treatise,* secs. 87, 123, 6. Also see secs. 25, 50, 94, 123, 137, 138, &c.

[10] Ibid., secs. 87, 131, 183. Also see secs. 88, 96, 97, 99, 129, 130, &c.

[11] Ibid., sec. 7.

rule to all men [which requires] the preservation of all mankind'.[12] The ethical theory in the *Treatise*, then, is both consistent and coherent; it is Strauss's method which is in error.[13]

Strauss considers Locke's few statements about property rights 'the central part of his political teaching' and added evidence for his Hobbesianism, for 'the natural right of property is a corollary of the fundamental right of self-preservation'.[14] He concludes that Locke sanctions 'unlimited appropriation without concern for the needs of others' because the only limitation to appropriation, that property should not be allowed to spoil, is removed in a civil society, where 'with the invention of money . . . each man can rightfully and without injury possess more than he himself can make use of'. 'According to the Natural Law [*sic!*]—and this means according to the moral law—man in civil society may acquire as much property of every kind and in particular as much money as he pleases.' Thus, Locke's doctrine 'is directly intelligible today if it is taken as the classic doctrine of "the spirit of capitalism", for by building society on the low but solid ground of selfishness one will achieve greater public benefits than by futilely appealing to virtue which is by nature unendowed'.[15]

The validity of Strauss's conclusion hinges on his establishing two points: first, that the right to acquire money is removed from the spoilage principle; and second, that this right is the archetype—and justification—for all property rights.

Locke's comments on money always have presented difficulties, for, on the one hand, he speaks of 'laying up', 'hoarding', 'heaping up',

---

12 Ibid., sec. 135.

13 Others have argued that Locke's normative law of nature sanctions egoism, for in sec. 6, and elsewhere, Locke says one should help others 'only when his own preservation comes not in competition'. This interpretation has the advantage of combining selfish interests with prudential obligations, the doctrine Strauss explicitly rejects but implicitly accepts; but two considerations can be brought against this position. First, there are only a few statements in which the law of nature is said to justify selfishness but there are over fifty references to its justifying concern for all mankind; hence, the latter must represent Locke's considered judgment and the former his inaccurate expression of it. Second, on this view, an individual would never join a civil society if he believed that most of his rights would be violated; but when he does join, Locke says he agrees that 'the fundamental natural law which is to govern even the legislative itself is the preservation of society and (as far as will consist with the public good) of every person in it' (sec. 134). Hence, an individual might have some, or most, or even all his rights violated and still accept the action as justified because it preserves the society. Men's obligations, then, are moral, not merely prudential.

14 Strauss, op. cit., pp. 234–5.

15 Ibid., pp. 240, 241, 243, 246–7.

'keeping', and 'possessing' money rather than 'investing', 'increasing', or 'acquiring' it as a good capitalist would. Moreover, he says money's chief function is to facilitate the exchange of goods, for it is 'some lasting thing that man would take in exchange for the truly useful but perishable supports of life'. And the spoilage principle still operates, for 'a man may rightfully and without injury possess more than he can make use of because it may continue long in his possession without decaying'.[16] So, clearly, Locke did not intend to be a capitalist.

Yet, one can rightfully ask what Locke would do with his 'heaped up' money, and answer, with him, use it for 'a disproportionate and unequal possession of the earth'; for 'continueing and enlarging his possessions'.[17] And other tracts, written during the same period, espouse a remarkably cogent capitalist theory.[18] So, clearly, Locke can be made, quite easily, into a capitalist.

The evidence, then, is not conclusive and hence Strauss's conclusion is not justified. But, the important point is not textual, whether there are limits to the accumulation of money; rather, it is philosophical, whether this account, now assumed to be correct, acts as prototype and justification for all property rights. Is the right to appropriate and retain property limited in any way?

If Locke on money is used to justify Locke on property, it is not remiss to note that money is mentioned in only five of 'On Property's' twenty-six sections suggesting, thereby, that Strauss is letting the tail wag the dog. Moreover, Locke frequently discusses property rights in other chapters but never again refers to money; perhaps the tail is wagging an elephant. Furthermore, it is simply not true that Locke sanctions unlimited appropriation and inalienable property rights. Again, he is quite explicit. When the legislature is not in session, the ruler may make laws for the common good,

for many accidents may happen wherein a strict and rigid observation of the laws may do harm (as not to pull down an innocent man's house to stop the fire when the next to it is burning) . . . the end of government being the preservation of all, as much as may be.

It is fit everyone who enjoys a share of protection should pay out of his estate his proportion for the maintenance of it. But still it must be with his own consent, i.e. the consent of the majority giving it either by themselves or their representatives.

---

16 *Treatise*, op. cit., secs. 47, 50, 36.
17 Ibid., secs. 48, 50.
18 See C. B. Macpherson's 'Locke on Capitalist Appropriation' in *Western Political Quarterly*, 1951, pp. 550–66, for an interesting exposition of this view.

[When a man leaves the civil society] he must quit the right which belongs to him by the laws of it and leave the possessions there descending to him from his ancestors.[19]

Thus, an individual *agrees* to have his house destroyed, his property confiscated, and his taxes decided by the majority because these acts preserve civil society. Locke makes these assertions because he believes men have obligations as well as rights, but Strauss ignores all such statements because he is convinced that a 'civil society merely creates the conditions under which individuals can pursue their productive-acquisitive activity without obstruction', i.e. men have no obligations.[20] Strauss's theory is interesting; unfortunately, it is not Locke's.

This does not exhaust Strauss's account of property rights or his total report on Locke, but it should be sufficient to show that his interpretation is both misleading and mistaken. Why has such a competent scholar made such grievous mistakes? The answer is as simple as it is obvious. The author of the definitive work on Hobbes's political theory must have found it easy to assume that Locke's presentation would be as rigorous and complete as Hobbes's, so when he failed to find precise definitions,[21] logical acumen, or complete analyses in the *Second Treatise* he felt compelled to scurry to Locke's other writings to patch together a theory Locke *might* have used. And when Locke's reconstructed natural law theory turned out to be inadequate, what better premiss to assert as basic than one which Locke occasionally suggests, and one which Strauss already knew intimately—Hobbes's egoism.

II

Two other 'non-traditional' interpretations warrant brief consideration. According to Willmoore Kendall, Locke's fundamental premiss is in his account of community life, for

whenever men live in a community with one another, the relations between them can be described in terms which, in addition to assigning to the whole

---

[19] *Treatise*, op. cit., secs. 159, 140, 191.
[20] Strauss, op. cit., p. 246.
[21] For instance, Locke stipulatively defines 'property' as: (1) 'estate'; (2) 'lives, liberties, and estates'; (3) 'the property which men have in their persons as well as their goods'; (4) 'life, liberty, health, limb, and goods'; and (5) 'life, liberty, and limb'. See secs. 123, 87, 173, 6, 137, 171.

community unlimited power, assigns to its numerical majority a *right* to make decisions which are binding upon all.[22]

Since 'the majority rule principle is, in a word, implicit in the logic of community life', it follows that 'the commonwealth's judgments are the individual's judgments *whether he agrees with them or not, i.e. they are the individual's judgments even when he consciously disagrees with them*'.[23] Men's rights, then, 'are such rights as are compatible with the public good which, in turn, is determined by the majority' and Locke is *really* advocating an extreme majority rule theory 'so authoritarian that no individualist could conceivably accept it'.[24]

As with all 'nothing but' interpretations, the adequacy of Kendall's account can be measured in two ways: is there any important aspect of Locke's thought which cannot be subsumed under the governing principle; and, does he consistently maintain his own interpretation? On both counts Kendall fails.

Consider the status of natural law. According to Kendall, 'men have an unlimited competence to modify the law of nature by agreement; for example: the agreement among men "to put a value on" money means, if it means anything at all, that the law of nature can be changed by unanimous agreement'.[25] Of course, the reference to unanimity does not necessarily support the claim for majority rule, for an action may be binding under the latter but not under the former. Moreover, this interpretation ignores such explicit statements as: 'The law of nature does not depend on the express consent of any of the commoners.'[26] Finally, Kendall confuses man's interpretation of the law with the law itself, man's understanding with God's understanding; for Locke does not suggest that human agreements, even unanimous ones, can alter pre-existent principles.

Or again, Kendall claims that when there is conflict between the individual's right to retain property and the community's right to use it, the spoilage principle requires that one 'unhesitatingly sacrifice the former to the latter'.[27] Textually, Kendall is in error, for Locke makes no such statement in the sections cited; in fact, in these sections Locke

---

[22] *John Locke and the Doctrine of Majority Rule*, Illinois University Studies in Social Sciences, Urbana, Illinois, 1941, vol. 26, p. 112. Italics in text.

[23] Ibid., pp. 66, 105. Italics in text.

[24] Ibid., pp. 112, 113. Also see pp. 58, 71, 78.

[25] Ibid., pp. 84–85.

[26] *Treatise*, op. cit., sec. 28.

[27] *Treatise*, secs. 31–36; Kendall, op. cit., p. 71.

repeatedly refers to a condition of plenty, hence there would be no conflict of rights. And even if there were, there is nothing in the spoilage principle to suggest that Locke 'unhesitatingly' accepts the alternative Kendall attributes to him. Indeed, why accept the spoilage principle at all? Kendall does not claim that majority rule is authoritative here; why, then, should one recognize its authority?

In fact, Kendall does not really believe that Locke can be squeezed into one principle. He begins his critique with the pronouncement: 'We are not, be it noted, denying that both elements, indefeasible individual rights (which are, of course, only a shorthand expression for objective moral standards) and decision making power in the majority are present in Locke's system.'[28] And this dualist interpretation seems to reflect his more considered judgment, for his last chapter explains how the two elements can be 'reconciled'.[29] But if there are two, then the majority rule principle alone is not sufficient: the best disproof for Kendall's interpretation is Kendall himself.

Kendall sees Locke as asserting obligations and denying rights; Charles E. Vaughan finds the positions reversed. He considers Locke's account of natural law most important, and since this law

proclaims itself to the heart of every individual, man comes into the world with a ready made knowledge of good and evil, a knowledge of his rights and obligations before he ever enters a civil society. [Therefore], each person is entitled to dictate his will to the state; to refuse his assent—and we can only conclude, his obedience also—to any law or executive act which does not square with the divinely ordained code which each man finds written in his heart and which he alone has the right to interpret.[30]

Thus, Locke is 'The Prince of Individualists', for he claims that individuals are bound by only those obligations they choose to recognize. Or, to restate but two of the implications:

Taxation, as commonly understood, is in no way to be justified.
The only kind of war which can be justified on Locke's premises is the war *pro aris et focis:* the war waged by the individual against a savage invader in defense of bare life and personal property. All other forms of war demand the sacrifice of individual life and property to the welfare of the

---

[28] Ibid., p. 54.
[29] Ibid., pp. 133–5. His answer, for what it is worth, is that Locke held a 'latent premise' that the proposition 'right is that which the majority wills' is equivalent to the proposition 'the majority always wills what is right'.
[30] *Studies in the History of Political Philosophy*, Manchester University Press, 1925, vol. i, pp. 164, 171–2.

state. And this is a demand which no state framed on Locke's principles has a right to make; and which, if made, no individual in his senses would dream of accepting.[31]

Vaughan is more shrewd than Kendall, for instead of reinterpreting every statement as an instance of the basic principle, he simply admits Locke's diversity—and then accuses him of inconsistency. When Locke says a citizen should pay taxes, join others in fighting a war, agree to have his house destroyed, or abide by majority rule, Vaughan reports the claimed obligations and then says Locke did not clearly understand his own doctrine. Accordingly, one cannot dispute Vaughan with documentation; he claims that these instances have nothing to do with Locke's *real* theory. But one can point out the implication: if men have no civil obligations, and fully three-fourths of the *Second Treatise* is concerned with man's rights and obligations in civil society, then most of Locke's political philosophy never should have been written or, since it was, should never be read, if his real theory is to be understood.

However, Vaughan's basic candor leads him to state, succinctly, the crucial problem for his interpretation. Locke is the Prince of Individualists *only* if every individual *qua* individual has complete knowledge of the law of nature, for

either the law of nature is not so effective an instrument as you would have us believe for curbing the passions of man and securing his peace and welfare, or the change from the state of nature to the civil society is an unnecessary, and therefore, an unwarranted revolution.[32]

Vaughan accepts the second alternative, for if every person has the sole right to interpret the law, he has no obligation to obey a civil society which interprets it for him; therefore, Locke's civil society is unnecessary and unwarranted.

But Locke's own account is closer to the first. The state of nature is full of 'fears and continual dangers', 'great inconveniences', 'mutual grievances, injuries, and wrongs'; in fact, without government, the law of nature is largely ineffectual.[33] Some people do not understand its provisions; others cannot apply the rules to specific cases; still others are torn between conflicting obligations; and many simply do not do

---

[31] *Treatise*, pp. 183, 198.
[32] *Studies*, pp. 165–6. Also see pp. 158–61, 201.
[33] *Treatise*, op. cit., secs. 90, 91, 127.

what they should. There is no 'common and uniform' interpretation of the law, no clear understanding of one's rights and obligations, hence men do not come to civil society with 'a fully developed moral sense', but precisely because they *lack* that sense. Hence, civil society is both necessary and justified; indeed, if it were not, political philosophy would be futile.

Vaughan's writing is persuasive, his logic tenacious, but he commits one fundamental error: he confuses the *how* with the *what*. He argues that since the law of nature is known only *by* an individual, the individual's interpretation is justified—and inalienable. But the argument is purely formal, for if natural law sanctioned watching sunsets or eating gollywompus meat, Vaughan's conclusion still holds, since only an individual can decide how many sunsets or how much meat. For Locke, however, the *content* of natural law, the moral rules men *should* recognize, is of most importance, for these injunctions provide the basis for understanding the rights and obligations necessary to a civil society.

III

In addition to their specific errors, these interpreters share a common misconception: that Locke's theory can be reduced to a simple 'nothing but' principle. Actually, his theory is exceedingly complex. This can be seen best by reducing all his assertions to their logical components.

1. *Consent*. Locke tells us that his purpose is to 'justify' the revolution restoring Parliamentary rule to England. To do so, he denies that the *right* to rule comes from God, the Divine Right of Kings theory, but affirms that it does come from the voluntary consent of the governed. His chief purpose, then, as many writers have said, was to establish a democratic theory of sovereignty whereby government would be made responsible to its citizens and hence not rule 'arbitrarily'.

1.1. However, this claim requires the prior assumption that citizens have a right to choose their rulers. How is this right justified? Obviously it is not a right granted by existent rulers, for they might not rule with consent; *de facto* is not identical with *de jure* rule. The right, therefore, must exist independently of political authority; it is a 'natural' right, a claim that man *qua* man enjoys.

1.2. Man, therefore, must have a logical, if not physical, pre-political existence: the 'state of nature'. In this condition each individual has the right to seek his own preservation, but he also has the obligation to help to preserve, or at least not to hinder, the preservation of other men.

1.3. These 'natural' rights and duties are justified in two ways:

1.31. All life is created, and destroyed, by God; hence He must desire the continued existence of all living beings.

1.32. By means of eternal moral rules, 'laws of nature', He has told men how they should treat each other: they should seek the preservation of all mankind.

1.4. Government by consent, then, is simply the best way for an individual to fulfil his 'natural' rights and obligations.

1.5. Any government so established has the right to interpret the law of nature for specific cases and every citizen has an obligation to obey its laws.

2. *Freedom*. In addition to the existence and authority of independent moral principles, Locke utilized several meanings of 'freedom'.

2.1. If men should not, but can, ignore the dictates of natural law, they have the ability to choose: in traditional terms, men possess 'free will'.

2.2. The right of self-preservation allows each freely to 'appropriate' property. Each may justifiably aggregate as much as he desires, provided only that he should neither acquire it by 'invading' his neighbour's share nor allow it to spoil. The right to free appropriation leads to:

2.21. The labour theory of value, for nature's bounty acquires value only when someone 'mixes' his labour with it; and

2.22. A *laissez faire* economic theory, for the right to property depends upon one's own efforts, each being responsible for his own preservation. Government has no obligation to provide for the slackers.

2.3. The distinction between *de facto* and *de jure* rules requires an opportunity to choose if the right is not merely formal. Locke attaches such importance to this that he provides for three such opportunities.

2.31. Men must believe that the limitations imposed by government are less onerous than anarchy. Most will reach this conclusion because of past experience, but those who choose anarchy when their neighbours form a government are not bound by the others' decision.

2.32. Those who prefer government still must choose its form. This involves:

2.321. An agreement about procedures, for until all can concur in a method for making decisions, no justified decisions can be made. Locke identifies this agreement with majority rule (although he says other mutually acceptable procedures could be justified) and, presumably, it is a unanimous accord, for nothing in 2.31 makes the majority's decision to accept majority rule binding upon all. And,

2.322. An agreement about people. Once the procedures have been accepted by all, the particular legislators can be chosen.

2.33. But even these two instances of voluntary consent are not sufficient, for the final test of any government is experience. In time, some may prefer the terrors of anarchy to the tyranny of the majority; hence the government's right to rule must be measured, continuously, against its purpose for ruling; government by consent allows the perpetual potential right to revolution.

2.34. For those born after government's establishment, the first two opportunities are supplanted by the doctrine of implied consent, but the continual right to reassess the government's achievements remains unaltered.

2.4. These agreements are identical with a contractual relation wherein the parties' rights and obligations are clearly recognized and mutually accepted.

3. *Equality*. Locke's theory also uses the concept of equality; again, in several senses.

3.1. Since God makes no distinctions among men, He must consider all to be of equal moral worth, hence His law admonishes men to seek both their own preservation and the preservation of others. This rule applies:

3.11. When there is no governmental force to ensure its recognition, and

3.12. When government does exist and the law can be enforced.

3.121. Legislators should always recognize this general moral rule when making laws and hence should not rule 'arbitrarily' or against the 'public good'.

3.122. An individual cannot justify revolution by claiming abrogation of his own rights; only a claimed violation of the rights of the majority gives sufficient reason for one to consider rebellion.

3.2. Each man's right to self-preservation allows him to appropriate property; his obligation to others limits his appropriation to what will not spoil. All, then, have an equal right to some degree of property and each has an obligation to see that the right is fulfilled.

3.3. Majority rule assumes that each person counts for one and only one vote in making political decisions and choosing legislators. Also, presumably, each should have an equal opportunity to become a legislator.

Consent; freedom; equality: these are the concepts from which Locke's political philosophy is made. Each is distinct: freedom to consent also implies freedom not to; economic freedom is different from (and incompatible with?) economic equality; consent does not necessarily imply the assumed equality of majority rule. Yet each is necessary: without consent the denials in the *First Treatise* and the affirmations in the *Second* would be incomprehensible; without freedom to exercise choice, the right to consent would be empty; without a theory of obligations, the establishment and continuance of government would be impossible. So, Locke's theory really involves three distinct, but interrelated, ideas; hence all attempts to explain it with a single 'nothing but' principle are doomed, *a priori*, to failure.

IV

If this brief analysis is even approximately correct, several conclusions seem justified.

One should not be surprised at the extent and assortment of differences which mark the writings of Locke's interpreters; his theory allows, indeed encourages, diverse explanations. Here he has been reported to be an anarchist and an authoritarian, a denier and an affirmer of natural law, an egoist and a majority rule advocate—and each writer can document his report with explicit statements. And this does not exhaust the possibilities. Others have seen Locke as a revolutionary, a traditionalist, a Whig, or a defender of inalienable rights and there is no reason why some shrewd observer, and competent scholar, should not see Locke's *real* theory as advocating Marxism, secession, or preserving the *status quo*. Actually, Locke's theory is so complex that writers can assert a variety of principles as basic—and with sufficient ingenuity find justification for their interpretation.

And this leads to a second conclusion. One does not need to be particularly astute to discover inconsistencies, for when statements originating from different basic concepts are laid side by side, incompatibilities become evident. Locke's theory requires both obedience to the state and the right to revolt: consent *v.* freedom. He sanctions unlimited appropriation, yet an obligation to help to preserve others: freedom *v.* equality. He relies upon majority rule, yet affirms the inalienability of an individual's consent: equality *v.* consent. It is no wonder, then, that some writers have concluded that Locke is 'a blundering incompetent' or 'a man whose problem exceeds his powers'.

Yet, these inconsistencies are not as serious as one might suppose. For one thing, a complex theory involves a number of different questions and some supposed inconsistencies have resulted from the failure to distinguish, for example, statements about the origin of government from statements concerning its moral efficacy, or descriptions of men's motivations from prescriptions of their rights. Moreover, as previously mentioned, Locke is not a careful writer, hence one does not get at the heart of his theory by documenting isolated snippets and minutiæ. An interpreter's scholarship must seek out the frequently repeated assertions and the broad outlines of the theory if he is to escape the inconsistencies resulting from Locke's carelessness.

But even after using appropriate scholarship, one will still find paradoxes, for the basic principles, themselves, are partially incompatible. Yet it should be pointed out that these inconsistencies form the basis for many of the haunting dilemmas in modern democratic governments. Should we grant Communists freedom of speech when we know that, in power, they abolish government by consent? Which would you deny, freedom or consent? Should the proceeds from a progressive income tax be used for slum clearance or farm subsidies; which is more important, freedom or equality? Should a conscientious objector be punished for refusing to support a war sanctioned by the majority; consent or equality? Each side justifies itself by appealing to basic democratic principles, hence *we* have no clear and ready answer to these problems. But if Locke's theory has inconsistencies precisely because it involves *all* these principles, we can conclude that criticisms of his theory are applicable far beyond the *Second Treatise* and that his unresolved difficulties still remain unresolved—and difficult.

One final point can only be suggested. Locke's theory actually involves a series of tensions, for these concepts supplement—and limit—each other both in theory and in history. Unlimited freedom is anarchy, but government initially established by consent can become tyrannical, hence, freedom must be restricted by consent; consent continually supplemented by freedom. Unlimited appropriation can lead to injustice, but total reliance upon the majority's beneficence can lead to apathy, so freedom is circumscribed by equality; equality complemented by freedom. Majority rule can be tyrannical, but a state with no commonly recognized procedures would be chaotic, so equality is countered by the right to review consent; freedom of conscience completed by equality. And in history, *laissez-faire* capitalism was challenged on the grounds of inequality and injustice; New Deal egalitarianism because it destroyed initiative and freedom; equal voting rights for negroes because those whites most affected will not consent. Locke's theory, then—and democratic government—have limits built into their framework, for when the consequences of any one concept become too important, an appeal to either, or both, the other two can be used to restore the balance.

Thus, both Locke's theory and democratic government's practice, are conducive to endless discussion and perpetual confusion, but also they have an inner source of vitality which makes the practice perennially adaptable and the theory continually interesting. Locke's theory, then, merely anticipates the problems of modern democratic government, so that in an even larger sense than the eighteenth-century writers realized, John Locke was the philosopher of democracy.

NATURAL RIGHTS*

William J. Wainwright

I

It may not be useful to distinguish natural rights from other rights. If one does choose to speak of natural rights (and many do), it is desirable to be as clear about them as possible. I propose to define natural rights as rights which meet three conditions. They must correspond to moral obligations, and these obligations must be both universal and important. Each of these conditions calls for some comment.

(A) Saying that natural rights correspond to obligations does not commit me to the view that wherever we have a right we have a corresponding obligation, but only to the view that wherever we have a natural right we have a corresponding obligation. Nor am I maintaining that wherever we have an important and universal moral obligation we have a natural right, but only that wherever we have an important and universal moral obligation, then, if there is a corresponding right, that right is a natural right.

(B) The moral obligations which correspond to natural rights are universal. By definition any moral obligation is universal in the sense that it is *prima facie* binding on anyone who is in the appropriate situation. Thus the obligation to keep promises is *prima facie* binding on anyone who has freely made a promise. Statements of moral obligation are universal or universalizable. We are not, however, interested in this sort of universality.

Someone who occupies a certain station in life may have moral obligations to those who stand in some special relation to him. Obligations of this sort are universal in the sense that anyone who occupies that station has certain definite obligations to anyone who stands in the special relation to him. But there are two senses in which these obligations are not universal. The obligations do not in fact fall on every man (or they fall on them only conditionally—*if* they ever occupy that

*Reprinted from the *American Philosophical Quarterly,* Vol. 4 (1967), 79–84, by permission of the editor and author.

station then they must . . .) and one has these obligations only toward certain persons (those who stand in the special relation). The demand that an obligation be universal may be, and I think sometimes is, a demand that it either fall on all men actually as well as conditionally (that it be universal with respect to its subject) or that it be an obligation of which all men are the object (that it be universal with respect to its object) or both.

1. What can it mean to say that an obligation actually falls on all men? It can mean at least two things: (a) That the obligation falls on man as man and not simply in so far as he plays a special role or enters into a special relation with someone, or (b) that the role or special relation which gives rise to the obligation is one which most men are likely to assume at one time or another, for example, by being a parent or entering into an agreement.

2. That an obligation is one of which all men are the object can also be understood in two ways. That is, (a) it can be understood as an obligation which we have toward a man simply because he is a man and not because, for example, he has merit or has entered into a contract with us. (The obligation to save a drowning man is, I suppose, universal in this sense.) Or (b) it can be understood as an obligation which is such that most men would at some time or other be the object of this obligation, for example, by being a child or the recipient of a promise.

We should notice that if an obligation is universal with respect both to its subject and its object, it is reasonable to suppose that it is one which actually and not simply conditionally applies in all societies (and this in the double sense that both subjects and objects of the obligation are to be met with in all societies).

If the obligation is one which falls on man as such, then it is an obligation which falls on men in all societies. If the obligation is universal with respect to its subject in the second sense, i.e., if it is an obligation which most men fall under at some time or other, then it is natural to expect that the obligation will fall on men in all societies. However, this is not necessarily the case, for it could be true of a given obligation both that it falls on most men at some time or other and that in some society it never falls on anyone. This observation suggests another sense in which an obligation could be universal with respect to its subject—viz., that it be an obligation which falls on most men at some time or other in *any* society. (Parental obligations or those arising from a promise *might* be obligations of this sort.) This in turn could be taken in at least two ways. "Any society" could be understood as meaning any actual society (past societies, present societies,

and those which are likely to arise in the future) or it could be understood as meaning any possible society. Thus we have four senses in
which any moral obligation is universal with respect to its subject. The
four senses are:

  i. that the obligation fall on man as man,
  ii. that it fall on most men at some time or other,
  iii. that it fall on most men at some time or other, in any actual society, and
  iv. that it fall on most men at some time or other in any possible society.

Corresponding to the four senses in which an obligation may be
universal with respect to its subject, we can distinguish four senses in
which an obligation may be universal with respect to its object:

  i. the obligation is to man as man,
  ii. it is such that most men would at some time or other be the object of
this obligation,
  iii. it is such that in any actual society most men will at some time be its
object, and
  iv. it is such that in any possible society most men will at some time be its
object.[1]

I have said that natural rights correspond to universal obligations.
We are now in a position to spell this out more clearly.

Natural rights may be provisionally defined as rights which
correspond to important moral obligations which are universal with
respect to their object in either the first or fourth senses and which are
universal with respect to their subject in either the first or fourth
senses.

(C) By definition any moral obligation is important in the sense
that it overrides (all?) non-moral obligations. Natural rights not only
correspond to moral obligations, and thus share in the importance
which is involved in any moral obligation, they correspond to the
more important of these obligations. One obligation is more important
than another if it generally overrides the other where there is a conflict
between the two.

The universality of the corresponding obligation might be
thought to be sufficient to distinguish natural rights from other rights,
particularly in view of the fact that even the less important obligations

---

[1] In saying that an obligation to do x is subject or object universal, I mean
that (all or most) men are subjects or objects of a *prima facie* obligation to do x.
I do not mean to deny that the obligation may be overridden by other obligations
in certain circumstances.

are important in the sense that they override all non-moral obligations. Importance has been made a condition for the following reason. I am inclined to think that "Be polite" is a moral rule. It is possible that the ground for having a code of etiquette, and this rule, would be found in all possible societies. The obligation would then be universal in the required sense. Furthermore, there seems to be nothing improper in speaking of a right to be treated politely (e.g., not to be insulted). A right, therefore, corresponds to the universal obligation. Nevertheless it seems a bit odd to speak of a natural right to be treated politely. If we introduce the notion of importance, we get out of this difficulty, for presumably politeness is not one of the more important obligations.

I would like to conclude this section of my paper by comparing my definition with two others with which it might be confused. The first is the notion that natural rights are those which must be respected if society is to endure. For an obligation to have subjects and objects in a possible society, all that is necessary is that the grounds occur in that society. It is not necessary that the obligation be respected or even recognized. Thus, even if there were a society which did not recognize the right to life, it could still be the case that the obligation has subjects and objects in that society and that it is important in that society, i.e., it could be true both that men in that society ought not to kill and that men in that society have a right to life, and that this obligation and right should be regarded as overriding in that society. From this it follows that an obligation can be important and universal in the required way (and thus that the corresponding right is a natural right) and yet not be recognized in some society. Now if a right is not recognized in some society, then respect for that right can hardly be a necessary condition of the survival of society. Therefore, if my definition of natural rights is correct, their recognition is not necessary for the survival of society. Furthermore, I do not think that the claim that natural rights are those which must be respected if society is to endure is at all plausible. Respect for a right cannot be a necessary condition of society if it is not recognized and more or less adhered to in all societies. To accept the claim would mean that nothing would count as a natural right which was not recognized in all societies and I do not believe that we wish to place this restriction on the notion of natural rights.

Margaret MacDonald suggests[2] that natural rights are the funda-

---

[2] Margaret MacDonald, "Natural Rights" in *Philosophy, Politics and Society*, ed. Peter Laslett (First Series, Oxford, Basil Blackwell, 1963), pp. 47–48.

mental conditions of a good society. If taken literally, this is probably false. The fundamental conditions for a good society may well include many things other than the recognition and fulfillment of certain obligations. For example, certain material and historical conditions may be necessary for a good society. On the other hand, since natural rights correspond to important moral obligations which occur in any possible society, and since no society can—perhaps analytically—be a good one which does not respect the important obligations which occur in that society, it follows that no society can be a good society which does not respect natural rights. Respect for natural rights is a necessary condition for a good society.

II

I shall now examine some of the rights which Locke considers to be natural rights. The purpose of this discussion will be to sharpen and qualify the remarks made in Part I.

(A) The right to life and the obligation not to take a human life rest on the claim that each of us is God's property.[3] If this is true at all, then it is true of each man in any possible society and the obligation will presumably be universal with respect both to its subject and its object in the first sense.

Liberty is also a natural right. To enslave another is to exercise the power of life and death over him. But because I have no right to take his life (he is God's property), I cannot have a right to enslave him.[4] Since the obligation not to kill another is universal with respect both to its subject and to its object in the first sense, it would seem that the obligation not to enslave another is also subject universal and object universal in the first sense.

But this will not do, for Locke says that men may forfeit their right to life and liberty if they unjustly attack another,[5] thereby cutting themselves off from the moral community.[6] This suggests that a necessary condition of the possession of the rights to life and liberty is membership in a community of rational beings who are governed by laws, either those of nature or those of political society.[7] If so, the

---

[3] John Locke, *Second Treatise on Civil Government*, para. 6.
[4] *Ibid.*, paras. 22–24.
[5] *Ibid.*, paras. 16–18, 23, 85.
[6] *Ibid.*, paras. 8, 10–11, 16.
[7] Cf. *ibid.*, para. 57.

ground for the right to life and liberty is not simply that one is God's property but also includes the fact that one is a member of a moral community in the sense required.[8] We have already seen that the first part of the ground will be found in all possible societies, but would the second part of the ground also be found in all possible societies?

A society most of whose members prey upon other communities is surely a possible society. In such a society most members would have unjustly resorted to violence and so would have forfeited (not have) the right to life and liberty. If my definition is correct, it would follow that life and liberty are not natural rights, for the corresponding obligations would not be object universal in either the first or fourth sense. We might conclude from this that my definition is inadequate. On the other hand, we might conclude that, contrary to Locke, refusing to resort to the unjust use of violence is not a ground for these rights. Or we might conclude that there is no natural right to life and liberty as such, but only a natural right to life and liberty in so far as one does not unjustly resort to violence. Members of a criminal society may well enjoy these rights.

(B) The primary ground for property rights is labor.[9] Locke also suggests gift,[10] bequest,[11] and exchange[12] as grounds for property rights. The obligations to respect property so acquired seem to be subject universal in the first sense. All men are obligated to respect property, i.e., one doesn't have to take up a special role or do something special or belong to a special society to come under this obligation. If gift, bequest, and exchange are sources of property rights, and labor is construed as broadly as Locke construes it (so as to include picking something up, gathering berries, etc.) then it is difficult to believe that there would be very many who would not have property in something in any possible society. If so, obligation will be object universal in the fourth sense.

(C) Parents have a right to exercise authority over their children during the minority of the child.[13] What obligation corresponds to

---

[8] This is not quite right, for infants and madmen are not members of the moral community in any full sense (paras. 57, 60) and yet they have a right to life. They have no right to liberty—to act autonomously—but presumably they do have a right not to be enslaved. The difference is perhaps this: children and madmen are potentially full members of the moral community, but those who unjustly resort to violence have wilfully severed their connections with it.

[9] Locke, *op. cit.*, paras. 27 ff.

[10] *Ibid.*, para. 46.

[11] *Ibid.*, para. 72.

[12] *Ibid.*, paras. 14, 46.

[13] *Ibid.*, para. 67.

this right? The right arises from the obligation to care for one's children, but this is not a corresponding obligation in the sense in question (where rights in one person correspond to obligations in another). If we take seriously the notion that one is under the natural law only if one has reason, and if children lack reason,[14] then the corresponding obligation is not the obligation to obey one's parents. The corresponding obligation will presumably be that of not interfering with the parents' direction of their children. The ground for this right and obligation is the obligation parents have to care for their children. This in turn is based on the fact that children lack reason and have been given by God to the parents as their responsibility.[15] (Freedom is justified only in so far as one is a full member of a community governed by laws, but full membership requires rationality which children lack.[16] Furthermore, since children lack reason, guidance is necessary for their own good.[17]) Would these grounds be found in any possible society?

There are two difficulties. In the first place, a society in which parents do not know their own children is a logically possible society. For example, the children are taken away at birth and raised in public institutions. No birth records are kept. In the second place, it is logically possible that there be a (human) society in which children have no parents. (They are raised in a test tube.) In either case, the obligation which corresponds to the right may still be subject universal in the first sense. All men may be obligated to refrain from interfering with a parent's direction of his children. On the other hand, in the first society parents do not direct their children and are unable to do so, except accidentally, because they do not know who their children are. It would, therefore, seem that the obligation has *no* objects in this society and is therefore not object universal in either the first or the fourth sense. It should be noticed, however, that the reason why the obligation has no objects in this society is to be found in the peculiar institutions of this society, and these institutions may be morally suspect. It is possible, though perhaps false, that wherever the grounds for this right and obligation do not occur, the absence of these grounds is itself a ground for moral criticism. In the second society there are no parents and hence no objects of the obligation in question. The obligation is not, then, object universal in either the first or fourth sense. But it should be noticed that it may still be true that the ground for the

---

[14] *Ibid.*, para 57.
[15] *Ibid.*, para. 56.
[16] *Ibid.*, para. 57.
[17] *Ibid.*, para. 63.

right and obligation will be found in any society which is at all likely
to occur. (The notion of a society which is at all likely to occur is to
be distinguished from that of an actual society mentioned in Part I.
Actual societies include past and present societies, and those which will
probably arise in the future. Societies which are at all likely to arise
include not only actual societies, but also all those societies the occurrence of which is not highly improbable. The dividing line between
the two conceptions is clearly not a sharp one.)

(D) Locke also asserts that children have an obligation to honor
and assist their parents on the grounds that they have been begotten
and nurtured by them.[18] Corresponding to this obligation, parents
have a right to these things.[19] I am inclined to think that Locke would
say that the obligation is object universal in the fourth sense. It arises
from the fact that parents have begotten and nurtured children and
this is something most, though not all, men will do in all possible
societies. Whether this is true or not would depend on whether the
ground is primarily the begetting or the nurture of children. If it is the
former, then the ground of the obligation will occur in any society
which is at all likely to occur (though not in all possible ones, since
societies without parents are logically possible). If it is the latter, then
it need not occur in any society which is at all likely to occur—whatever the concept of a society which is at all likely to occur includes, it
surely includes a society where the children are nurtured by the
community. But even though the obligation to honor and assist one's
parents might not be object universal, either in the sense that it has
objects in all possible societies or in the sense that it has objects in any
society which is at all likely to occur, the individual's obligation to
honor and respect the ones who have nurtured him may be, for presumably in any possible society there would be objects of this obligation.[20] At the same time, there could well be a society in which a
relatively few people were involved in nurturing the children, and if
this were the case it would not be true that *most* people in all possible
societies were the object of this obligation.

If the primary ground for the obligation is that one has been

---

18 *Ibid.*, para. 66.
19 *Ibid.*, para. 67.
20 One might object that the nurture of children is not a *logically* necessary
condition of a human society. I am inclined to think that childhood (involving
nurture and guidance of some sort) is (logically) necessary for a human existence
in a way in which begetting children and being begotten by human parents is
not. I am, however, by no means clear on this point.

begotten by one's parents, the right will not be subject universal in either the first sense or the fourth sense because of the possibility of a parentless society. However, all men will be under it in any society which is at all likely to occur. If the ground for the obligation is nurture, then it need not be subject universal in either the first or fourth sense nor in the sense that persons would be subject to this obligation in any society which is at all likely to occur, for there may be societies in which parents do not nurture their children. On the other hand, an obligation to honor and assist those who have nurtured you will be subject universal in the first sense (if we may suppose that all men must be nurtured to a greater or less degree by someone or other).

(E) Our discussion of Locke has suggested that there may be senses of universality other than those which are suggested in Part I. These senses are:

   v. the obligation has (many) subjects and objects in any society which is at all likely to occur,
  vi. the obligation has (only) some subjects and objects in any possible society,
 vii. the obligation has (only) some subjects and objects in any society which is at all likely to occur, and
viii. any society in which the obligation does not have (many or some) subjects or objects is such that the features which constitute reasons why there are no subjects and objects are grounds for moral criticism.

Should we abandon our provisional definition and extend the notion of natural rights so as to include rights which correspond to important obligations which are universal in any or all of these senses? I am inclined not to do so, on the grounds that natural right theorists have had a very strong sort of universality in mind and that the provisional definition is therefore closer to what has traditionally been meant by "natural rights." However, it seems to me to make little difference whether or not we extend the notion of natural rights in the ways suggested, as long as we are clear as to just what we are doing.

(F) Are the obligations which correspond to the rights we have discussed important obligations? The obligations not to kill, enslave or steal from another are surely important. The obligation to assist, honor, and respect one's parents and the obligation not to interfere with a parent's direction of his children seem less important. In particular the last obligation seems to be one which could be easily overridden by other more important obligations. I am not sure whether it is

more plausible to deny that the last is a natural right or to drop the
notion that a natural right must correspond to a more important
obligation.[21]

III

I should now like to say something about the connection between
the notion of natural rights and the notion of a state of nature. The
concept of a state of nature can be used in at least two ways. It can be
used to argue for the necessity of political society by pointing out the
disadvantages which men would suffer if there were no political
society. The notion of a state of nature can also be used in another
way, for it may be argued that by examining man in a state of nature
we can discover natural rights and obligations in the defined sense.
Locke uses the concept of a state of nature in both these ways.

If we look at our characterization of natural rights we can see the
plausibility of the second move. Natural rights correspond to obligations which fall on men in any society and whose objects can be found
in any society. The picture of a state of nature can (in part) be
regarded as an attempt to sketch features common to all societies.
(Examples of such features might be parental relationships, work,
agreements entered into, etc.) If these features are the grounds of
certain rights and obligations, one may conclude that these rights and
obligations are universal in the required sense, that they will hold in
any society. Furthermore, if these rights and obligations are overriding
in the state of nature, we may expect them to be overriding in all
societies. This is not, however, strictly necessary, for the special
arrangements of some society could be such that the obligation or
right arising from one of the common features was generally out-
weighed in that society though not in others.

For the purpose of determining natural rights in the defined sense
it is not essential that the state of nature be a state without government. The picture will be drawn without government only if political

---

[21] We might have considered (putative) natural rights other than those
mentioned by Locke. We might, for example, have considered the rights mentioned in the U.N. Declaration. I think that an examination of these rights would
show that they correspond to important obligations which are subject and object
universal in sense (i) or in one of the senses (iv) through (viii). It is difficult,
however, to determine in just what senses a corresponding obligation is universal
without determining what the grounds of the obligation are. In examining Locke,
one has the advantage that the grounds are given.

society is considered to be adventitious, i.e., if political society is not considered necessary to human society. That the state of nature has in practice been pictured as a state without government is due both to the fact that political society was considered accidental or adventitious and to the fact that the examination of a state of nature was serving a double purpose—furnishing reasons for the necessity of government as well as a doctrine of natural rights.

When the state of nature is pictured as society with government abstracted, we have another meaning of "natural rights," viz., "natural rights" are those moral rights, perhaps the most important ones, which obtain in a state of nature whether or not these rights carry over into, or remain important in, political society. (The right to judge one's own case would be an example of a right which one has in the absence of judicial institutions and which does not carry over into political society.) It is to be noticed, however, that if a right does not carry over into political society or if it loses its importance in political society, then it is not a natural right in the defined and, I venture to say, important sense.

It is true that Locke is interested in drawing a distinction between those rights and obligations which arise in nonpolitical society and those which arise in political society. It is not clear that we should be interested in this. In the first place, it may well be that any possible society is a political society. (This of course does not imply that certain rights may not be grounded in the nonpolitical aspects of society.) In the second place, Locke is interested in natural rights largely because he is interested in showing that there are (should be) restraints on arbitrary power. Yet the only rights which will function in this way are those which carry over into political society and are thus natural rights in my sense. Finally, natural rights are usually thought to be rights which all or most men have. If this is the case, rights which hold only in a state of nature cannot be natural rights.

THE SOCIAL BEARING OF LOCKE'S POLITICAL THEORY*

C. B. Macpherson

SOME UNSETTLED PROBLEMS OF LOCKE'S POLITICAL THEORY

The reference in the title of this paper is to be taken in a double sense. It marks a concern both with the social assumptions that carry the weight of Locke's political theory and with the type of society to which that theory pointed the direction. Not enough attention has been given to either of these problems, especially the first—the social assumptions. It is not entirely surprising that these assumptions have been neglected. The renewed discussion of Locke's political ideas in recent years is part of a revival of interest in natural law and in the meaning and possibilities of liberal democracy. But the current revival of interest in liberal-democratic principles contains its own dangers. It is, directly or indirectly, part of the Western defenses against communism. The consequent preoccupation with the broad validity of liberal democracy has inhibited any substantial notice of the class content of even seventeenth century liberal theory. Attention has thus been diverted from the social assumptions of Locke's theory, insofar as they are assumptions about the class character of society, in a way which is unlikely to be conducive to a valid understanding either of his theory or of liberal-democratic principles.

The neglecting of social bases alone might not call for a reinterpretation of Locke, were it not that current interpretations leave at the heart of his political theory serious unexplained inconsistencies. Neglect of Locke's social assumptions and failure to explain contradictions in his political theory are not unrelated. This paper attempts in part to show that a closer analysis of these assumptions may render Locke's political theory more intelligible.

* From the *Western Political Quarterly*, Vol. 7 (1954), 1–22. Reprinted by permission of the University of Utah, copyright owners.

The prevailing view, it might fairly be said, is that Locke was primarily the theorist of the liberal state, of constitutional or limited government as opposed to arbitrary or absolute government, of government conditional on the consent of the governed, or of majority rule qualified by individual rights. It is usually implied that the problem Locke had set himself was either to build a universally valid general theory of political obligation or to provide a general validation of a particular constitutional position. In either of these versions, little attention is given to the social, as distinct from the constitutional, content of Locke's theory.

Such abstraction from social content has not always prevailed. A more realistic quality was given to the constitutional interpretation by those who saw Locke's state as, in effect, a joint-stock company whose shareholders were the men of property. This was the view taken by Leslie Stephen in his *English Thought in the Eighteenth Century* (1876), by C. E. Vaughan in his *Studies in the History of Political Philosophy* (1925), by Laski in his *Locke to Bentham* (1920) and his *Rise of European Liberalism* (1936), and by Professor Tawney in his *Religion and the Rise of Capitalism* (1926). There is one great difficulty in this view. Who were the members of Locke's civil society? If they were only the men of property, how could the social contract be an adequate basis of political obligation for all men? Yet undoubtedly the purpose of the social contract was to find a basis for all-inclusive political obligation. Here is an outstanding difficulty. That eminent historians of thought did not see it as such is probably because their interpretation was mainly in the constitutional tradition:[1] it emphasized the limits Locke put on government in the interests of property, rather than the very great power Locke gave to the political community (his "civil society") as against individuals.

Another view, with opposite emphasis, has made some headway in the last ten years, following the publication of Professor Kendall's study.[2] There a strong case is made that Locke's theory confers something very close to complete sovereignty on civil society, that is, in

---

[1] Professor Tawney's, of course, was not, and he did draw attention to the decisive seventeenth century assumption that the laboring class was a race apart (R. H. Tawney, *Religion and the Rise of Capitalism* [Harmondsworth and New York: Penguin Books Ltd., 1940], pp. 175, 241, to which reference is made below, p. 64). However the implications for the political theory of the period, not being central to his argument, were not explored.

[2] Willmoore Kendall, *John Locke and the Doctrine of Majority-Rule* (Urbana, Illinois: University of Illinois, 1941).

effect, on the majority of the people (though not, of course, on the government, which has only fiduciary power). Against this sovereignty of the majority, the individual has no rights. Impressive evidence can be shown for this reading of Locke. It leads to the striking conclusion that Locke was not an individualist at all, but a "collectivist" in that he subordinated the purposes of the individual to the purposes of society. He is made a forerunner of Rousseau and the General Will.[3] The case is a strong one. However, in concluding that Locke was a "majority-rule democrat," this interpretation overlooks all the evidence that Locke was not a democrat at all. It reads into Locke a concern with the democratic principle of majority rule, which was to be the focus of much American political thinking in the late eighteenth and early nineteenth centuries, as it is now. And it leaves a major problem: Does not majority rule endanger that individual property right which Locke plainly sought to protect? Moreover, it proposes a resolution of Locke's many inconsistencies by imputing to him an assumption ("that the chances are at least 50 plus out of 100 that the average man is rational and just"),[4] which Locke certainly did not hold unambiguously and which he specifically contradicted more than once.[5]

More recently, attempts have been made, notably by J. W. Gough,[6] to bring Locke back into the liberal-individualist tradition. However, these efforts are not conclusive. In trying to rescue Locke from the abstract logical treatment he has had at some hands and to restore his theory to its historical context, the emphasis is again put on his constitutionalism. But the context of political history overshadows that of social and economic history. At most, what is proposed is a compromise between Locke's individualism and his "collectivism," and major inconsistencies are left unexplained.

Indeed, almost all interpretations fail to account for radical contradictions in Locke's postulates. Why should Locke have said, and what could he have meant by saying, both that men on the whole are rational and that most of them are not; both that the state of nature is rational, peaceable and social, and that it is not essentially different

---

[3] *Ibid.*, pp. 103–6.
[4] *Ibid.*, pp. 134–35.
[5] *Second Treatise of Civil Government*, sections 21, 123; and see below p. 76.
[6] J. W. Gough, *John Locke's Political Philosophy: Eight Studies* (Oxford, 1950).

from Hobbes's state of war?[7] To make consistency the first rule of interpretation is as unrealistic as to take comfort in the allegation that great minds are not consistent. Yet the contradictions that lie on the surface of the *Second Treatise of Civil Government* deserve more explanation than they have had. The fact that they cannot be resolved by logical analysis, or explained by constitutional historical analysis, suggests that they are the outcome of a deeper social contradiction. Therefore we may look to Locke's view of his own society for insight into the meaning of his political theory.

We shall find that his conception of that society, especially of its class differentiation, entered into his abstract postulates about the nature of society and man in a way that has not generally been noticed. This view goes far to account for the contradictions in Locke's political theory, and for the outstanding problems of its interpretation.

LOCKE'S SOCIAL PRECONCEPTIONS

Locke did not make all his social assumptions explicit. There is no reason why he should have done so. The assumptions which he and his contemporary readers absorbed from the thinking of their own time, and from their understanding of their own society, he could take for granted.

Here I want to direct attention to two preconceptions which Locke, in common with many others of his class and time, entertained about his own society. As assumptions about the nature of seventeenth century society they are explicit in various writings of Locke; as assumptions about society in general they are implicit in the *Treatise* and had a decisive influence in his political theory.[8]

These are (1) that while the laboring class is a necessary part of the nation, its members are not in fact full members of the body politic and have no claim to be so; and (2) that the members of the laboring

---

[7] *Rational* is used here in Locke's sense of governing oneself by the law of nature or law of reason (e.g., *Second Treatise*, § 6: Reason *is* the law of nature; § 8: To transgress the law of nature is to live by another rule than that of reason and common equity). For Locke's contradictory views of man's rationality, see below, pp. 74–78.

[8] These two are not necessarily Locke's most fundamental social assumptions. First place should be given to his belief that every man is the sole proprietor of his own person and capacities. But as this is explicit in the *Treatise*, it does not demand the same attention here. (See below pp. 71–72, 82–83.)

class do not and cannot live a fully rational life. "Laboring class" is used here to include both the "laboring poor" and the "idle poor," that is, all who were dependent on employment or charity or the workhouse because they had no property of their own by which, or on which, they might work.

That these people were not, in fact or by right, full members of political society was the prevailing view in England in the second half of the seventeenth century. They were regarded not as citizens but as a body of actual and potential labor available for the purposes of the nation. Professor Tawney has summarized their position in the observation that the prevailing attitude of English writers after 1660 "towards the new industrial proletariat [was] noticeably harsher than that general in the first half of the seventeenth century, and . . . has no modern parallel except in the behaviour of the less reputable of white colonists towards coloured labour."[9] The working class was, in effect, in but not of civil society.

This attitude may be seen as a secularization, not only of the Puritan doctrine of the poor, but also of that Calvinist view in which the church, while claiming to include the whole population, held that full membership could be had only by the elect. The nonelect (who were mainly, though not entirely, coincidental with the nonpropertied) were at once members and not members of the church: not full members sharing in the government of the church, but sufficiently members to be subject, rightfully, to its discipline.[10] This Calvinist position tended to exclude beggars, vagrants, and all unemployed poor from full citizenship, an implication of their exclusion from full membership in the church.

The secular view that came to prevail during the Restoration went much further. Not only the unemployed but also the employed poor were treated, not as citizens but as objects of state policy. Economic writers of the day admitted, even insisted, that the laboring poor were the ultimate source of any nation's wealth, but only if they were compelled to continuous labor. That the arrangements for extracting this labor were not regarded as entirely satisfactory in 1688 is evident from Gregory King's famous statistical estimate of the population and income of England in 1688 (which, as Unwin has said, affords "better evidence of the common assumptions of the directing classes

[9] Tawney, *op. cit.*, pp. 240–41.
[10] For expressions of this view in English Calvinism, see Christopher Hill, "Puritans and the Poor," *Past & Present*, II (November, 1952), 41.

than of any objective social facts").[11] He divided the whole body of the people into those increasing and those decreasing the wealth of the kingdom, and put not only "cottagers and paupers" and "vagrants," but also the "labouring people and outservants" among the occupational classes, each of which decreased the wealth of the kingdom.[12]

The estimated size of the propertyless wage-earning and unemployed classes in 1688 need not be emphasized, though it is striking enough: King and D'Avenant put more than half the population in this category. What is more important is the assumption that the laboring class is to be managed by the state in order to make it productive of national gain. The laboring class's interests were not subordinated to the national interest; the class was not considered to have an interest. The ruling-class view of the national interest was the only one.

This attitude towards the working class, generally explicit in the economic writings of the period from 1660, is nicely exemplified in William Petyt's statement:

People are . . . the chiefest, most fundamental and precious commodity, out of which may be derived all sorts of manufactures, navigation, riches, conquest and solid dominion. This capital material being of itself raw and indigested is committed into the hands of supreme authority in whose prudence and disposition it is to improve, manage and fashion it to more or less advantage.[13]

The view that human beings of the laboring class were a commodity out of which riches and dominion might be derived, a raw material to be worked up and disposed of by the political authority, was fully shared by Locke. The evidence leaves no doubt that he regarded the working class as subject to, but without full membership in, the political society of seventeenth century England. He assumed this not only as a matter of fact but as a matter of right. The moral assumption was that the laboring class does not and cannot live a rational life.

[11] George Unwin, *Studies in Economic History* (ed. by R. H. Tawney, London, 1927), p. 345.
[12] King's estimate is conveniently reproduced in Dorothy George, *England in Transition* (Penguin edition, 1953), pp. 150–51. It is partially reproduced in G. N. Clark, *The Wealth of England from 1496 to 1760* (London, 1946), but without the division into those increasing and those decreasing. The full table is in D'Avenant's *Works* (1771), II, 184.
[13] William Petyt, *Britannia Languens* (1680), p. 23. This and similar passages from various writers of the period are quoted in E. S. Furniss, *The Position of the Laborer in a System of Nationalism* (New York: Houghton, 1920), pp. 16 ff.

Evidence of these assumptions is scattered throughout Locke's writings. His proposals for the treatment of the able-bodied unemployed are fairly well known, although when they are mentioned by modern writers it is usually to deprecate their severity and excuse it by reference to the standards of the time. What is more to the point is the view which these proposals afford of Locke's assumptions. Masters of workhouses ("houses of correction") were to be encouraged to make them into sweated-labor manufacturing establishments; justices of the peace were to make them into forced-labor institutions. Children of the unemployed "above the age of three" were unnecessarily a burden on the nation; they should be set to work, and could be made to earn more than their keep. All this was justified on the explicit ground that unemployment was due not to economic causes but to moral depravity. The multiplying of the unemployed, Locke wrote in 1697 in his capacity as a member of the Commission on Trade, was caused by "nothing else but the relaxation of discipline and corruption of manners."[14] There was no question in his mind of treating the unemployed as full or free members of the political community; there was equally no doubt that they were fully subject to the state. The state was entitled to deal with them in this way because they would not live up to the moral standard required of rational men.

Locke's attitude towards the employed wage-earning class has been noticed less often, though it is plain enough in various passages of his economic writings, particularly in *Some Considerations of the Consequences of the Lowering of Interest and Raising the Value of Money* (1691). There, incidentally to his technical arguments, Locke takes for granted that the wage-laborer constitutes a normal and sizable class in the nation,[15] that he has no property but is entirely dependent on his wages, and that, of necessity, his wages are normally at a bare subsistence level.[16] Such a person "just lives from hand to mouth." One passage in particular deserves quotation:

. . . The labourer's share [of the national income], being seldom more than a bare subsistence, never allows that body of men, time, or opportunity to raise their thoughts above that, or struggle with the richer for

---

[14] Quoted in H. R. Fox Bourne, *The Life of John Locke* (London, 1876), II, 378. Locke seems to have regarded the idle poor as depraved by choice, in contrast to the laboring poor, whom he considered incapable of a fully rational life because of their position. (See below, pp. 69–70.)

[15] *Considerations*, in *Works* (1759 edition), II, 13–16.

[16] *Ibid.*, p. 29.

theirs (as one common interest), unless when some common and great distress, uniting them in one universal ferment, makes them forget respect, and emboldens them to carve to their wants with armed forces: and then sometimes they break in upon the rich, and sweep all like a deluge. But this rarely happens but in the male-administration of neglected, or mismanaged government.[17]

It is hard to say which part of these remarks is the most revealing. There is the assumption that the laborers are normally kept too low to be able to think or act politically. There is the assertion that maladministration consists not of leaving them there, but of allowing such unusual distress to occur as will unite them in armed revolt. And there is the conviction that such revolt is improper, an offense against the respect they owe to their betters.

Now the question: Who has the right of revolution? is a decisive question with Locke. The revolutionary right is to him the only effective test of citizenship, as he makes no provision for any other method of overthrowing an unwanted government. Although he insists, in the *Treatise*, on the majority's right to revolution, it does not seem to cross his mind here that the laboring class might have the right to make a revolution. Indeed there is no reason why such a thought should have occurred to him, for to him the laboring class was an object of state policy and of administration, rather than fully a part of the citizen body. Such a class was incapable of rational political action, but the right to revolution depended essentially on rational decision.

The assumption that members of the laboring class are in too low a position to be capable of a rational life—that is, capable of regulating their lives by those moral principles Locke supposed were given by reason—is evident again in *The Reasonableness of Christianity*. The whole argument of that work is a plea that Christianity be restored to a few simple articles of belief "that the labouring and illiterate man may comprehend." Christianity should thus again be made

a religion suited to vulgar capacities; and the state of mankind in this world, destined to labour and travel. . . . The greatest part of mankind have not leisure for learning and logick, and superfine distinctions of the schools. Where the hand is used to the plough and the spade, the head is seldom elevated to sublime notions, or exercised in mysterious reasoning. 'Tis well if men of that rank (to say nothing of the other sex) can comprehend plain propositions, and a short reasoning about things familiar to their minds,

[17] *Ibid.*, p. 36.

and nearly allied to their daily experience. Go beyond this, and you amaze the greatest part of mankind. . . .[18]

This is not, as might be thought, a plea for a simple rationalist ethical religion to replace the disputations of the theologians. On the contrary, Locke's point is that without supernatural sanctions the laboring class is incapable of following a rationalist ethic. He only wants the sanctions made clearer. The simple articles he recommends are not moral rules, but articles of faith. Belief in them is all that is necessary, for such belief converts the moral rules of the gospel into binding commands. Locke's problem is to frame the articles so that they will appeal directly to the experience of the common people, who can thus believe.[19] The greatest part of mankind, he concludes, cannot be left to the guidance of the laws of nature or of reason; they are not capable of drawing rules of conduct from them. For "the day-labourers and tradesmen, the spinsters and dairy-maids . . . hearing plain commands, is the sure and only course to bring them to obedience and practice. The greatest part cannot know and therefore they must believe."[20]

Of course, Locke was recommending this simplified Christianity for all classes, as may be seen in his ingenuously mercantile observations on the surpassing utility of the Christian doctrine of rewards and punishments.

The [ancient] philosophers, indeed, shewed the beauty of virtue; . . . but leaving her unendowed, very few were willing to espouse her. . . . But now there being put into the scales on her side, 'an exceeding and immortal weight of glory'; interest is come about to her, and virtue now is visibly the most enriching purchase, and by much the best bargain. . . . The view of heaven and hell will cast a slight upon the short pleasures and pains of

---

[18] *The Reasonableness of Christianity*, last two pages; *Works* (1759), II, 585–86.

[19] The essential articles of belief are that there is a future life and that salvation can only be had by believing that Christ was raised from the dead to be the divine savior of mankind. Locke argues that this is a plain notion which, along with miracles, can readily be grasped by the illiterate in terms of their common experience: "The healing of the sick, the restoring sight to the blind by a word, the raising, and being raised from the dead, are matters of fact, which they can without difficulty conceive, and that he who does such things, must do them by the assistance of a divine power. These things lie level to the ordinariest apprehension: he that can distinguish between sick and well, lame and sound, dead and alive, is capable of this doctrine." (*Ibid.*, II, 580.)

[20] *Ibid.*, II, 580.

this present state, and give attractions and encouragements to virtue, which reason and interest, and the care of ourselves, cannot but allow and prefer. Upon this foundation, and upon this only, mortality stands firm, and may defy all competition.[21]

No doubt Locke's readers would appreciate this recommendation of Christianity more than would the laborers, who were not in a position to think in terms of making "the most enriching purchase." However, Locke regards as only a secondary advantage the ability of his fundamental Christian doctrine to satisfy men of higher capacities. His repeated emphasis on the necessity of the laboring classes being brought to obedience by a belief in divine rewards and punishments leaves no doubt about his main concern. The implication is plain: the laboring class, beyond all others, is incapable of living a rational life.

Clearly, then, when Locke looked at his own society he saw two classes with different rationality and different rights. It would have been strange had he not done so. Locke was no Leveller. His was not the democratic puritanism that had appeared during the Commonwealth, but the puritanism which had encountered no difficulty in accommodating itself to the exigencies of class rule in 1660. Locke had welcomed the Restoration not only because it had put an end to the turbulence of the Commonwealth,[22] but also because it had restored something that was positively good,

the protection of those laws which the prudence and providence of our ancestors established and the happy return of his Majesty hath restored: a body of laws so well composed, that whilst this nation would be content only to be under them they were always sure to be above their neighbours, which forced from this world this constant acknowledgment, that we were not only the happiest state but the purest church of the latter age.[23]

From this unreserved approbation of the pre-Commonwealth constitution—not, of course, the constitution (of Church and State) as understood by James I and Charles I, but as understood by the Parliamentarians—he went on to state as a matter of principle that "the supreme magistrate of every nation what way soever created, must necessarily

[21] *Ibid.*, II, 582.
[22] See the passages quoted from Locke's MS treatise of 1660 on the Civil Magistrate, in Gough, *op. cit.*, p. 178.
[23] Preface to the treatise on the Civil Magistrate, 1660; Bodleian Library, MS Locke C 28, fol. 2 verso.

have an absolute and arbitrary power over all the indifferent actions of his people."[24] Locke showed himself to be truly conservative in 1660. From then on, his view of society was that of the men of substance.

THE SOCIAL PRECONCEPTIONS GENERALIZED

It would be surprising if Locke's preconceptions about his own society did not somehow affect his premises about society and man as such. His unhistorical habit of mind presented no obstacle to his transferring assumptions about seventeenth-century society into a supposed state of nature. As he took his assumptions about his own society so much for granted that he felt no need to argue them, they could easily be carried into his premises without any consciousness of a problem of consistency. I shall argue that both of the assumptions about his own society—that of a class differential in rationality, and that of a class differential in rights—were generalized in Locke's thinking into implicit assumptions about human nature as such and about individual *natural* rights, and that these assumptions modified his explicit postulates about human nature and natural rights.

In Locke's initial statement of his postulates in the *Treatise* (and in his analysis of human nature in the *Essay Concerning Human Understanding*, which has to be considered also for a full statement of his general theory of human nature), there is nothing to suggest an assumption of class differentiation. However, before he used these postulates to deduce the necessary character of civil society, he put

----

24 *Ibid.,* fol. 3 recto. The difference between this and the position Locke took three decades later in the *Second Treatise* is not in the amount of power granted to the civil authority but in the locus of that power. The "absolute and arbitrary power" of 1660 is only over "indifferent actions." Indifferent actions he defined as those not comprehended in the law of nature or divine revelation; in other words, those matters as to which man is naturally free. (See Locke's premises, quoted in Gough, *op. cit.,* p. 179.) These are precisely the matters which in the *Second Treatise* Locke has the individual hand over to the supreme civil authority, there the civil society itself.

But in 1660 Locke was willing to consider a monarch—or was it only the king-in-parliament?—as the supreme authority; the "magistrate" is defined as "the supreme legislative power of any society, not considering the form of government or number of persons wherein it is placed" (MS treatise on Civil Magistrate, Bodleian Library, MS Locke, e. 7, fol. 1, sidenote); whereas in 1689 Locke reserved supreme authority to the civil society itself. He was consistent throughout in wanting a civil authority which could secure the basic institutions of a class society. In 1660 this required the recall of the Stuarts and the doctrine of the magistrate's absolute and arbitrary power in things indifferent; in 1689 it required the dismissal of the Stuarts and the doctrine of the *Second Treatise.*

forward other arguments, especially in his treatment of property rights, which imply that he had already generalized his differential assumptions about his own society into abstract implicit assumptions of differential human nature and natural rights.

(1) *Differential Rights.* We have seen that Locke found in seventeenth-century society a class differentiation so deep that the members of the laboring class had very different effective rights from the classes above them. They lived, and must live, "from hand to mouth," could never "raise their thoughts above that," and were unfit to participate in political life. Their condition was a result of their having no property on which they could expend their labor; their having no property was one aspect of the prevailing inequality which was grounded in "the necessity of affairs, and the constitution of human society."[25]

What Locke saw in his own society he considered typical of all civil society. But how did this become an assumption of differential *natural* rights, and where does it, as such an assumption, enter into the argument of the *Treatise?* It is certainly not present in the opening statements about natural rights; there the emphasis is all on the natural equality of rights (§§ 4, 5).[26]

The transformation of equal into differential natural rights comes to light in Locke's theory of property. In the chapter on property in the *Treatise*, he went out of his way to transform the natural right of every individual to such property as he needed for subsistence and to which he applied his labor, into a natural right of *unlimited* appropriation, by which the more industrious could rightfully acquire all the land, leaving others with no way to live except by selling the disposal of their labor.[27]

This transformation is not an aberration in Locke's individualism but an essential part of it. The core of his individualism is the assertion that every man is naturally the sole proprietor of his own person and capacities (§§ 4, 6, 44, 123)—the absolute proprietor in the sense that he owes nothing to society for them—and especially the absolute proprietor of his capacity to labor (§ 27). Every man is therefore free to alienate his own capacity to labor. This individualist postulate is the

---

[25] *Considerations, Works* (1759), II, 19.

[26] This and subsequent references in the text are to the section numbers of the *Second Treatise of Civil Government.* Quotations are from the 1764 edition of the *Treatises.*

[27] "Locke on Capitalist Appropriation," *Western Political Quarterly*, IV, 550–66.

one by which Locke transforms the mass of equal individuals (rightfully) into two classes with very different rights, those with property and those without. Once the land is all taken up, the fundamental right not to be subject to the jurisdiction of another is so unequal between owners and nonowners that it is different in kind, not in degree: those without property are dependent for their livelihood on those with property and are unable to alter their own circumstances. The initial equality of natural rights, which consisted in no man's having jurisdiction over another (§ 4) cannot last after the differentiation of property. In other words, the man without property in things loses that proprietorship of his own person which was the basis of his equal natural rights. Locke insists that disparity in property is *natural*, that is, that it takes place "out of the bounds of society, and without compact" (§ 50). Civil society is established to protect unequal possessions, which have already in the natural state caused unequal rights. In this way Locke has generalized the assumption of a class differential in rights in his own society into an implicit assumption of differential *natural* rights. This implicit assumption, as will be seen, did not replace the initial theory of equality: both were in Locke's mind at the same time.

(2) *Differential Rationality*. We have seen that Locke assumed in his own society a class differential in rationality which left the laboring class incapable of a fully rational life. The questions are: How did this become an assumption of differential rationality in general? And where did this enter the argument of the *Treatise?* It is clearly not present in the opening statements and postulates. There, rationality and depravity are dealt with abstractly and although rational men are distinguished from depraved men,[28] there is no suggestion that the distinction is correlated with social class. But as the argument proceeds and the postulates have to be made more specific, it becomes apparent that Locke has something else in mind. When he has to relate depravity and rationality to man's political needs, these qualities turn out to have meaning only in the setting of a particular kind of property institutions and to be closely related to ownership.

Whatever man's inherent depravity may be, Locke thinks it does not require any but the most rudimentary political society until there is extensive property. Where there was "the equality of a simple poor way of living, confining [men's] desires within the narrow bounds of each man's small property," there would be few controversies and few trespasses, and consequently no need of many laws or magistrates;

[28] See below, p. 75.

there would be more fear of outsiders than of each other, and the main purpose of setting up government would be for security "against foreign force" (§ 107). A fully civil society of the kind which is the main concern of the *Treatise,* a society for the internal security of individual property, is required for the protection not of small equal properties but only of extensive unequal ones, not of a modest store of consumables or perhaps a few acres of land but of a substantial accumulation of resources. It is the propensity to accumulate property beyond the requirements of subsistence that necessarily leads rational men to establish civil society.

Here we reach the crux of the matter. The propensity to accumulate, although it leads to quarrels, is itself not depraved but rational. Not only is the desire for accumulation rational, according to Locke, but accumulation is the essence of rational conduct. More precisely, the true nature of rational behavior is to expend labor improving the gifts of nature for subsequent enjoyment of greater real income or of greater power or prestige. This procedure, in Locke's view, requires private possession; and the measure of rational industriousness is the accumulation of possessions.

All this can be seen in the famous chapter on property in the *Treatise,* the burden of which is that the truly rational man is the industrious man. Rational behavior in temporal affairs is investing one's energies in the accumulation of real property and capital. "God gave the world to men in common; but . . . he gave it them . . . for . . . the greatest conveniences of life they were capable to draw from it. . . ." Therefore, He "gave it to the use of the industrious and rational," who would "improve" it (§ 34). Improvement without ownership is impossible: "The condition of human life, which requires labour and materials to work on, necessarily introduces private possessions" (§ 35). Not everyone in the state of nature could acquire property, for wherever money is introduced—and it is introduced in the state of nature (§ 50)—the land is all appropriated (§ 45). That the appropriation leaves some men without any possibility of getting land does not disturb Locke because the day-laborer in a society where the land is all appropriated is better off than the greatest man in a primitive economy (§ 41).

Thus "the industrious and rational" are not all laborers, but only those who acquire property and improve it by their labor.[29] A further

---

[29] The same conclusion is reached, from a different starting point, by Leo Strauss, in a penetrating recent article on natural law: "On Locke's Doctrine of Natural Rights," *Philosophical Review,* XLI (October, 1952), 495–96.

effect of the introduction of money is that the rational goal of a man's industry becomes accumulation beyond any requirements of consumption. "Different degrees of industry" give men different amounts of property, and the invention of money gives the more industrious man the opportunity "to enlarge his possessions beyond the use of his family, and a plentiful supply to its consumption" (§ 48). In short, rational conduct, in the state of nature, consists in unlimited accumulation, the possibility of which is open only to some. It follows that there was, in Locke's view, a class differential in rationality in the state of nature, inasmuch as those who were left without property after the land was all appropriated could not be accounted fully rational. They had no opportunity to be so. Like day laborers in civil society they were not in a position to expend their labor improving the gifts of nature; their whole energies were needed to keep alive. They could not "raise their thoughts above that," for they just lived "from hand to mouth."

THE AMBIGUOUS STATE OF NATURE

From the foregoing analysis it may be concluded that Locke read back into the state of nature, in a generalized form, the assumptions he made about differential rights and rationality in existing societies. Although the generalized assumptions modified in his own mind the initial postulates of the *Treatise*, they did not displace them. Locke entertained both at the same time, at different levels of consciousness. Hence, the postulates on which he was operating were confused and ambiguous. All men were on the whole rational; yet there were two distinct classes of rationality. All men were equal in natural rights; yet there were two distinct orders of possession of natural rights. The source of the extraordinary contradiction in Locke's presentation of human nature is found here.

We customarily think that Locke held men to be essentially rational and social. Rational, in that they could live together by the law of nature, which is reason, or which at least (though not imprinted on the mind) is knowable by reason without the help of revelation. Social, in that they could live by the law of nature without the imposition of rules by a sovereign. This conception, indeed, is usually said to be the great difference between Locke's and Hobbes's views of human nature. If there is a significant difference it is here that one expects to find it, rather than in the theory of motivation. For Locke, like Hobbes, held that men are moved primarily by appetite and aversion; the appetites are so strong that "if they were left to their full swing, they would carry men to the overturning of all morality. Moral laws are set as a curb and restraint to these exorbitant desires."[30] It is usually maintained that the difference between this and Hobbes's view is that Locke thought men capable of setting these rules on themselves, by perceiving their utility, without installing a sovereign.

The general theory presented at the opening of the *Treatise* affirms that men are naturally able to govern themselves by the law of nature, or reason. The state of nature, we are told, has a law of nature to govern it, which is reason (§ 6). The state of nature is contrasted flatly to the state of war: the two are "as far distant, as a state of peace, goodwill, mutual assistance and preservation, and a state of enmity, malice, violence and mutual destruction, are from one another. Men living together according to reason, without a common superior on earth, with authority to judge between them, is properly the state of nature" (§ 19). It is no derogation of this view of the state of nature to allow, as Locke does, that there are some men in it who will not follow the law of nature. Nature's law teaches only those who will consult it (§ 6); some men transgress it and, by so doing, declare themselves "to live by another rule than that of reason and common equity" and in this way become "dangerous to mankind" (§ 8); a man who violates the law of nature "becomes degenerate, and declares himself to quit the principles of human nature, and to be a noxious creature" (§ 10). The whole picture of the state of nature in chapter ii of the *Treatise* is one of a people abiding by natural law, with some natural criminals among them: Locke even uses the word criminal to describe the man in the state of nature who violates its law (§ 8).

But this representation is only one of two quite opposite pictures Locke has of the state of nature. As early as chapter iii of the *Treatise*, only a page after the distinction between the state of nature and the state of war, we read that where there is no authority to decide between contenders "every the least difference is apt to end" in the "state of war," and that "one great reason of men's putting themselves into society, and quitting the state of nature" is "to avoid this state of war"

---

[30] *Essay Concerning Human Understanding*, I, 3, § 3. Cf. Locke's Hobbesian reflection in 1678 that "the principal spring from which the action of men take their rise, the rule they conduct them by, and the end to which they direct them, seem to be credit and reputation, and that which at any rate they avoid is in the greatest part shame and disgrace," and the consequences he draws for government. (Quoted from Locke's MS journal in Fox Bourne, *op. cit.*, I, 403–4.)

(§ 21).[31] The difference between the state of nature and the Hobbesian state of war has virtually disappeared. Some chapters later, we read further that the state of nature is "very unsafe, very unsecure"; that in it the enjoyment of individual rights is "very uncertain, and constantly exposed to the invasion of others," and that it is "full of fears and continual dangers." All this danger occurs because "the greater part [are] no strict observers of equity and justice" (§ 123). What makes the state of nature unlivable, according to this account, is not the viciousness of the few but the disposition of "the greater part" to depart from the law of reason.

The contradiction between Locke's two sets of statements about natural man is obvious. It is a central contradiction in the explicit postulates on which his political theory is built. It will not do to say he simply echoes the traditional Christian conception of man as a contradictory mixture of appetite and reason. Locke no doubt accepted that view; and within it there is room for a considerable variety of belief as to the relative weights (or potentialities) of the two ingredients of human nature. Different exponents of Christian doctrine could take different views. What has to be explained is how Locke took not one position in this matter but two opposite positions.

One might say that he had to take both in order to make his case against Hobbes; he had to make men rational enough not to require a Hobbesian sovereign, yet contentious enough to necessitate their handing over their natural rights and powers to a civil society. However, to say this would be to accuse Locke, unjustly and unnecessarily, either of intellectual dishonesty or of extraordinary superficiality; besides, it would imply an underestimate of the extent to which Locke did subordinate the individual to the state.[32]

It seems more reasonable to conclude that Locke was able to take both positions about human nature because he had in mind simultaneously two conceptions of society, which, although logically conflict-

---

[31] This passage is not in the Everyman edition of the two Treatises (ed. by W. S. Carpenter) nor in the Appleton-Century edition of the *Second Treatise* and *Letter Concerning Toleration* (ed. by C. L. Sherman, New York, 1937). Each of these follows, at this point, a printing of the first edition of the *Treatises* which did not contain any § 21, and each has covered up the deficiency by arbitrarily dividing another section into two. (Sherman divides § 20: Carpenter divides § 36, so that all the sections in the Everyman edition from 21 to 35 are wrongly numbered.) The particulars of the two printings of Locke's first edition, and of their handling by modern editors, are given in Peter Laslett's "The 1690 Edition of Locke's *Two Treatises of Government:* Two States," *Transactions of the Cambridge Bibliographical Society*, IV (1952), 341–47.

[32] See below, p. 81.

ing, were derived from the same ultimate source. One was the seventeenth-century atomistic conception of society as a mass of equal, undifferentiated beings. The other was the notion of a society composed of two classes differentiated by their level of rationality—those who were "industrious and rational" and had property, and those who were not, who labored, indeed, but only to live, not to accumulate.

Locke was unconscious of the contradiction between these two conceptions of society because both of them (and not merely, as we have already seen, the second one) were elements transferred to his postulates from his comprehension of his own society. Ultimately it was Locke's comprehension of his own society that was ambiguous and contradictory. It could not have been otherwise, for it was the comprehension of an emerging bourgeois society, reflecting the ambivalence of a society which demanded formal equality but required substantive inequality of rights.

As a bourgeois philosopher, a proponent of seventeenth-century individualism, Locke had to regard men as equal, undifferentiated units, and to consider them rational. The bourgeois order justified itself by assuming, first, that all men were intellectually capable of shifting for themselves, and secondly, that rational behavior in this sense was morally rational, in accordance with the law of nature. Thus a necessary part of the bourgeois vision pictured man in general in the image of rational bourgeois man. Locke shared this view, which gave him the account of the state of nature as rational and peaceable.

At the same time, as a bourgeois philosopher Locke necessarily conceived abstract society as consisting of two classes with different rationality. The two classes in Locke's England lived lives totally different in freedom and rights. The basic difference between them in fact was the difference in their ability to live by the bourgeois moral code. But to the directing class this appeared to be a differential capacity in men to live by moral rules as such. This conception of society gave Locke the picture of the state of nature as unsafe and insecure. For to say, as he did, that most men are incapable of guiding their lives by the law of reason, without sanctions, is to say that a civil society with legal sanctions (and a church with spiritual sanctions) is needed to keep them in order. Without these sanctions, i.e., in a state of nature, there could be no peace.

Both views of the state of nature flowed from the bourgeois concept of society, and both were necessary to it. Their common source obscured their contradictory quality. There was no question of Locke's basing his theory on an Aristotelian concept of two classes—

masters and slaves—whose relative positions were justified by a supposed inherent difference in rationality. With Locke the difference in rationality was not inherent in men; it was socially acquired by virtue of different economic positions. But since it was acquired in the state of nature, it was inherent in society. Once acquired, that is to say, it was permanent, for it was the concomitant of an order of property relations which Locke assumed to be the permanent basis of civilized society. His notion of differential rationality justified as natural, not slavery,[33] but the subordination of one part of the people by their continual contractual alienation of their capacity to labor. In the bourgeois view men were free to alienate their freedom, and Locke, at least, thought that the difference in rationality was a result rather than a cause of that alienation. But the difference in rationality, once established, provided a justification for differential rights.

THE AMBIGUOUS CIVIL SOCIETY

We may now inquire how Locke's ambiguous position on natural rights and rationality enters and affects his theory of the formation of civil society. Men enter into civil society, Locke asserts, to protect themselves from the inconveniences, insecurity and violence of the state of nature. Or, as he declares repeatedly, the great reason for men's uniting into society and putting themselves under government is to preserve their property, by which, he says, he means their "lives, liberties and estates" (§ 123, cf. § 173). When property is so defined, everyone has a reason to enter civil society, and everyone is capable of entering it, having some rights which he can transfer. However, Locke did not keep to this definition. He used the term in two different senses at points where its meaning was decisive in his argument. The property for the protection of which men oblige themselves to civil society is sometimes (e.g., §§ 123, 131, 137) stated to be "life, liberty and estate," but sometimes (e.g. § 138–140) it is clearly only goods or land.[34] Consequently, men without estate or goods, that is, without

---

[33] Locke did, of course, justify slavery also, but not on grounds of inherently differential rationality. Enslavement was justified only when a man had "by his fault forfeited his own life, by some act that deserves death" (§ 23). Locke appears to have thought of it as a fit penalty for his natural criminals.

[34] A striking instance of the latter use is in § 138, where, after arguing that men in society must have property (since the purpose of their entering society was to preserve property), he concludes that "they have such a right to the goods which by the law of the community are theirs, that nobody hath a right to take

property in the ordinary sense, are rightfully both in civil society and not in civil society.

When the property for the protection of which men enter civil society is taken to be life, liberty and estate, all men (except slaves) are eligible for membership; when it is taken to be goods or estate alone, then only men who possess them are eligible. Locke interprets it both ways, without any consciousness of inconsistency. What has happened is understandable in the light of our analysis. Locke's recognition of differential class rights in his own society, having been carried into his postulates as an implicit assumption of differential natural rights and rationality, without displacing the formal assumption of general rationality and equal rights, has emerged at the level of the social contract in a crucial ambiguity about who are parties to the contract.

The question as to whom Locke considered to be members of civil society seems to admit only one answer. Everyone, whether or not he has property in the ordinary sense, is included, as having an interest in preserving his life and liberty. At the same time only those with "estate" can be full members, for two reasons: only they have a full interest in the preservation of property, and only they are fully capable of that rational life—that voluntary obligation to the law of reason—which is the necessary basis for full participation in civil society. The laboring class, being without estate, are subject to, but not full members of, civil society. If it be objected that this is not one answer but two inconsistent answers, the reply must be that both answers follow from Locke's assumptions, and that neither one alone, but only the two together, accurately represent his thinking.

This ambiguity about membership in civil society by virtue of the supposed original contract allows Locke to consider all men as members for purposes of being ruled and only the men of estate as members for purposes of ruling. The right to rule (more accurately, the right to control any government) is given only to the men of estate; it is they who are given the decisive voice about taxation, without which no government can subsist (§ 140). On the other hand, the obligation to be bound by law and subject to the lawful government is fixed on all men whether or not they have property in the sense of estate, indeed, whether or not they have made an express compact. When Locke broadens his doctrine of express consent into a doctrine of tacit consent, he leaves no doubt about who are obligated. Tacit

---

their substance or any part of it from them without their own consent; without this they have no property at all."

consent is assumed to have been given by "every man, that hath any possessions, or enjoyment, of any part of the dominions of any government . . . whether this his possession be of land, to him and his heirs forever, or a lodging only for a week; or whether it be barely travelling freely on the highway; and in effect, it reaches as far as the very being of any one within the territories of that government" (§ 119). Locke is careful to say (§ 122) that this does not make a man a full member of civil society, but only subjects him rightfully to its government: the men of no estate are not admitted to full membership by the back door of tacit consent.[35] Of course, Locke had to retreat to tacit consent because it was impossible to show express consent in the case of present citizens of an established state. However, his doctrine of tacit consent has the added convenience that it clearly imposes obligation, reaching to their "very being," on those with no estate whatever.

It appears from the foregoing analysis that the result of Locke's work was to provide a moral basis for a class state from postulates of equal individual natural rights. Given the seventeenth-century individualist natural-rights assumptions, a class state could only be legitimized by a doctrine of consent which would bring one class within, but not make it fully a part of, the state. Locke's theory achieved this end. Its accomplishment required the implicit assumptions which he held. These assumptions involved him in the ambiguities and contradictions that pervade his argument. It is difficult to see how he could have persisted in such contradictions had he not been taking the class state as one desideratum and equal natural rights as another.

Locke did not twist deliberately a theory of equal natural rights into a justification for a class state. On the contrary, his honestly held natural-rights assumptions made it possible, indeed almost guaranteed, that his theory would justify a class state without any sleight of hand. The decisive factor was that the equal natural rights Locke envisaged, including as they did the right to unlimited accumulation of property, led logically to differential class rights and so to justification of a class state. Locke's confusions are the result of honest deduction from a postulate of equal natural rights which contained its own contradiction. The evidence suggests that he did not realize the contradiction in the postulate of equal natural right to unlimited property, but that he

---

[35] We may notice incidentally that in his discussion of tacit consent, as well as in that of the supposed express entry into civil society by the contract, Locke lumps together life, liberty and estate under one term, and here the term is not even "property" but "possession" (§ 119, quoted above).

simply read into the realm of right (or the state of nature) a social relation which he accepted as normal in civilized society. The source of the contradictions in his theory is his attempt to state in universal (nonclass) terms, rights and obligations which necessarily had a class content.

UNSETTLED PROBLEMS RECONSIDERED

When Locke's theory is understood in the sense here ascribed to it, some outstanding difficulties of its interpretation may be resolved.

(1) The problem inherent in the joint-stock interpretation of Locke's state is now no problem, for we have seen how Locke considers that the state consists both of property-owners only and of the whole population. He has no difficulty, therefore, in thinking of the state as a joint-stock company of owners whose majority decision binds not only themselves but also their employees. The laboring class, whose only asset is their capacity to labor, cannot take part in the operations of the company at the same level as the owners. Nevertheless, the laboring class is so necessary to the operations of the company as to be an organic part of it. The purpose of the company is not only to keep the property it has, but also to preserve the right and conditions which enable it to enlarge its property; one of these conditions is a labor force effectively submitted to the company's jurisdiction. Perhaps the closest analogue to Locke's state is the joint-stock company of merchants trading with or planting in distant lands, whose charter gives them, or allows them to take, such jurisdiction over the natives or the transplanted labor force as the nature of the trade requires.

(2) The implicit contradiction in that interpretation of Locke's theory which emphasizes the supremacy of the majority is also explained. The inconsistency, it will be remembered, was between the assertion of majority rule and the insistence on the sanctity of individual property. What would happen if the propertyless were a majority? This was no fanciful problem. It had been raised in the debates between the Levellers and the Independents in the parliamentary army during the civil wars.[36] It was a real difficulty in Locke's day, for it was thought that the propertyless were a majority.[37]

[36] A. S. P. Woodhouse, ed., *Puritanism and Liberty* (London: Dent, 1938), esp. pp. 53–63.
[37] Cf. King's estimate, cited above, n. 12.

We can now see that there is no conflict between the assertion of majority rule and of property right inasmuch as Locke was assuming that only those with property were full members of civil society and thus of the majority.

(3) Various inconsistencies left unexplained in Locke by the liberal-individualist interpretation can also be resolved. Mr. Gough asks, for instance, whether Locke can really have believed, as he did (§ 140), "that the consent of a majority of representatives was the same as a man's own consent, from which it is, in fact, twice removed?"[38] Locke can easily have thought so if he was thinking primarily of the defense of property owners as a whole. His equation of a man's own consent with the consent of the majority makes sense only if he was thinking in this way. Locke was very well aware that there were differences of interest between the landed men, the merchants, and the monied men, differences which he saw sharply demonstrated in struggles over the incidence of taxation.[39] In these circumstances, the fact that he could identify individual and majority consent to taxation indicates that he was thinking of the defense of property as such. Locke could assume, as a man of property himself, that the common interest of propertied men was more important than their divergent interests as owners of land, or of money, or of mercantile stock.

(4) The debate about whether Locke was an individualist or a "collectivist," whether he put the purposes of the individual or the purposes of society first, now appears in a new light. When the fundamental quality of Locke's individualism is kept in mind, the controversy becomes meaningless. His individualism does not consist entirely in maintaining that individuals are by nature free and equal and can only be rightfully subjected to the jurisdiction of others by their own consent. The main significance of Locke's individualism is that it makes the individual the natural proprietor of his own person and capacities, owing nothing to society for them.

Such an individualism is necessarily collectivism (in the sense of asserting the supremacy of civil society over every individual). For it asserts an individuality that can be realized fully only in accumulating property, and, therefore, realized only by some at the expense of the individuality of the others. To permit such a society to function, political authority must be supreme over individuals; if it is not, there

38 *Op. cit.*, p. 69.
39 *Considerations, in Works* (1759), II, 36, 29.

can be no assurance that the property institutions essential to this kind of individualism will have adequate protection. Individuals who have the means to realize their personalities (that is, the propertied) do not need to reserve any rights against civil society, since civil society is constructed by and for them, and operated by and for them. All they need to do is insist that civil society, or the majority of themselves, is supreme over any government, for a particular government might otherwise get out of hand. Locke did not hesitate to allow individuals to hand over to civil society all their natural rights and powers, including specifically all their possessions and land (§§ 120, 128, 136), or, what comes to the same thing, to grant all the rights and powers necessary to the ends for which society was formed (§§ 99, 129, 131), the majority being the judge (§ 97). The wholesale transfer of individual rights was necessary to get sufficient collective force for the protection of property. Locke could afford to propose this transfer because the civil society was to be in the control of the men of property. Under these circumstances individualism must, and could safely, be left to the collective supremacy of the state.

The notion that individualism and "collectivism" are the opposite ends of a scale along which states and theories of the state can be arranged, regardless of the stage of social development in which they appear, is superficial and misleading. Locke's individualism, that of an emerging capitalist society, does not exclude, but on the contrary demands, supremacy of the state over the individual. It is not a question of the more individualism, the less collectivism; rather, the more thoroughgoing the individualism, the more complete the collectivism. Hobbes's theory is the supreme illustration of this relation, but his denial of traditional natural law and his failure to provide guarantees for property against the sovereign (whether a majority of the people or an absolute monarch) did not recommend his views to those who thought property the central social fact. Locke was more acceptable because of his ambiguity about natural law and because he provided some sort of guarantee for property rights. When the specific quality of seventeenth-century bourgeois individualism is seen in this light, it is no longer necessary to search for a compromise between Locke's individualist and collectivist statements; they imply each other.

(5) Locke's constitutionalism now becomes more intelligible; it need not be minimized or emphasized. It can be seen for what it is, a defense of the rights of expanding property rather than of the rights of the individual against the state.

We may notice, in this respect, that Locke did not think it desirable (whereas the Levellers in the Agreement of the People had thought it essential) to reserve some rights to the individual against any parliament or government. Locke's state does not directly protect any individual rights. The individual's only safeguard against arbitrary government lies in the right of the majority to say when a government has broken its trust to act always in the public good, never arbitrarily. Locke could assume that this supremacy of the majority constituted a sufficient safeguard for individual rights because he thought that all who had the right to be consulted were agreed on one concept of the public good: maximizing the nation's wealth, and thereby (as he saw it) its welfare. This agreement could be postulated only because he thought that the laboring class had no right to be consulted. Locke's constitutionalism is essentially a defense of the supremacy of property—not that of the yeoman only, but more especially that of the men of substance to whom the security of unlimited accumulation was of first importance.

Locke's insistence that the authority of the government ("the legislative") is limited and fiduciary, dependent on the consent of the majority of taxable persons, or on that majority's interpretation of the government's faithfulness to its trust, is not the primary part of his whole theory. He had to develop limitations on government because he had first constructed the other part, i.e., the total subordination of the individual to civil society. Both parts were necessary for any theory which sought to protect and promote the property institutions, and thereby the kind of society, which to secure a civil war, a restoration, and a further revolution had been necessary. If in 1689 the confinement of arbitrary government had a more obvious immediacy, subordination of the individual to the state had at least as lasting a significance. The Whig revolution not only established the supremacy of parliament over the monarchy but also consolidated the position of the men of property—specifically of those men who were using their property in the new way, as capital employed to yield profit—over the laboring class. Locke's theory served the Whig state in both respects.

We have seen how Locke, by carrying into his postulates the implicit assumptions of class differential rationality and rights (derived from his comprehension of his own society), reached an ambiguous theory of differential membership in civil society, a theory which justified a class state from postulates of equal individual natural rights. Ambiguity about membership concealed from Locke himself the contradiction in his individualism, which produced full individuality for some by consuming the individuality of others. Locke could not have been conscious that the individuality he championed was at the same time a denial of individuality. Such consciousness was not to be found in men who were just beginning to grasp the great possibilities for individual freedom which lay in the advancement of capitalist society. The contradiction was there, but these men could not recognize it, let alone resolve it. Locke was at the fountainhead of English liberalism. The greatness of seventeenth-century liberalism was its assertion that the free rational individual was the criterion of the good society; its tragedy was that this very assertion necessarily denied individualism to half the nation.

LOCKE AND THE
DICTATORSHIP OF THE
BOURGEOISIE*

Alan Ryan[1]

It is a commonplace, but true, that the two terms on which Locke rests the greatest weight of doctrine in the *Second Treatise* are 'consent' and 'property'. It is with the second of these terms that we are here concerned, and in particular with the use which Locke makes of his doctrine that:

> The great and *chief end* therefore, of Mens uniting into Commonwealths, and putting themselves under Government, *is the Preservation of their Property*.[2]

There has been a good deal of criticism levelled at Locke's account of property from one direction or another. Complaints of wild and absurd individualism[3] contrast with assertions of his collectivist leanings.[4] Complaints about his obsession with history that never happened[5] contrast with assertions of his intense interest in, and the great importance to his theory of, sociology, history and anthropology,[6] in as genuine a form as the seventeenth century knew them. Here we shall concentrate on a different issue, namely on the extent to which it is true that Locke's account of property, and his resultant account of natural rights, political obligation, and the proper functions of government, form an ideology for a rising capitalist class. My question is

---

* Reprinted from *Political Studies*, Vol. 13 (1965), 219–230, by permission of the Clarendon Press, Oxford.

[1] I should like to say how much I owe to the late G. A. Paul in this paper; it amounts to a good deal as to doctrine, and all but everything as to method.

[2] See 124, cf. (all refs. to Laslett edition).

[3] Vaughan: *Studies in the History of Political Philosophy*.

[4] Kendall: *John Locke and Majority Rule*.

[5] Gough: *John Locke's Political Philosophy*.

[6] Cox: *Locke on War and Peace*.

How far does what Locke says in the *Second Treatise* substantiate Macpherson's[7] thesis that he was providing—perhaps no more than half-consciously—a moral basis for the dictatorship of the bourgeoisie?

One initial clarification of the scope of my discussion of this question is needed. Macpherson uses a good deal of material from outside the *Second Treatise* to substantiate his view of it. Indeed his working assumption seems often enough to be that we should look for Locke's political theory outside the *Second Treatise* and then see if previously ambiguous passages in that work (numerous enough on anyone's reading) will square with the theory obtained elsewhere. This may be a method appropriate to a historical inquiry into Locke's political intentions; it may yield the historian a coherent and convincing answer to the question of what Locke *really meant*. Here, however, I take the alternative path of attempting to find within the *Second Treatise* alone some coherent doctrine of political right and obligation, based on what Locke says there about property. Such an account may perhaps be in danger of refutation by the historian as an account of *what* Locke *intended*. It is in less, even no, danger of contradiction from such a quarter as an account of *what Locke said*. And in case this is thought too small a claim, let me point out that we usually hold people to what they say, rather than to what they may suppose to follow from what they meant to say.

The essence of Macpherson's account is that Locke intends to supply the moral basis of that stage of economic advance which we have called the dictatorship of the bourgeoisie; this is a state of unrestrained capitalism, brutal in its treatment of the labouring classes, ruthless in its destruction of traditional values, of all social ties that impede the advance of the propertied classes. Locke is thus arguing for nothing less than the rightful absolute power of the propertied classes, for a morally justified tyranny of the employers over the employed. Indeed, the labouring and the unemployed classes have their rights so ruthlessly eroded that their status is to be subject to civil society without being full members of it; they are in it but not of it. The state of nature that Locke envisages must therefore be such that these elements of the bourgeois state follow from it. Crediting Locke as no-one has done before, with a logically rigorous deduction of civil society from the state of nature, Macpherson argues that everything in the state of nature conceived by Locke was put there by him for the

---

[7] Macpherson: *Political Theory of Possessive Individualism*, cp. V. cf. *Western Political Quarterly* 1951 and 1954.

purpose of generating some feature or other of bourgeois society. The misery, the viciousness, and the instabilities of the resulting society are attributed to 'contradictions' put into the state of nature by Locke. I need not emphasize how different is this Locke from the one we have met before.

I

The twin pivots upon which Macpherson's account turns are the premises he ascribes to Locke of the natural proprietorship of one's own labour, and the dependence of freedom and morality, and hence of citizenship, upon the possession of rationality. These are, of course, important elements in Locke's political theory; to Macpherson they account for the whole of this theory. They are central, vital, and closely connected. Rationality is evinced by (sometimes it seems that Macpherson is saying it is identified with) the ability to acquire goods and go on acquiring them up to the limits set by the Law of Nature. A rational man is one who obeys the law of Reason, and the law of reason is in turn the Law of Nature, and this is the will of God. Given such a gloss on what it is to be rational, the argument clearly runs that it is morally excellent to accumulate, that success in accumulating is a moral virtue, and hence that the man of property is of greater moral worth than the man without property. In the state of nature before the invention of money the title to property is given by labour, for in the state of nature each man is originally the unconditional owner of his own labour. This doctrine is, on Macpherson's account of it, an important and indeed a decisive break with medieval attitudes to labour and property, which were concerned to emphasize the obligations of a man to society and to his fellows, not his rights against them. So the rational man sets about accumulating property, and because his right to it is derived from his absolute right to his own labour, this right is absolute, too.

If it is labour, a man's absolute property, which justifies appropriation and creates rights, the individual right of appropriation overrides any moral claims of the society. The traditional view that property and labour were social functions and that the ownership of property involved social obligations, is thereby undermined.[8]

8 Macpherson p. 221.

Thus Locke secures the right to unlimited accumulation. But in the state of nature before the invention of money there are two limitations upon the exercise of this right. The first is that 'enough and as good' must be left for others,[9] which one may call the *sufficiency limitation*. The second is that nothing may spoil in the hands of the person who gathers it:

> As much as any one can make use of to any advantage of life before it spoils; so much he may by his labour fix a Property in. Whatever is beyond this, is more than his share, and belongs to others. Nothing was made by God for Man to spoil or destroy.[10]

This we may call the *spoliation limitation*. There is a third apparent limitation imposed by the labour criterion of ownership, namely that a man must mix his labour with whatever he appropriates.[11] This limitation lies at the heart of what one might call 'radical' labour theories of value, where the intention is to deny any title to property other than the title of manual labour. The obvious similarity between Locke's premises and those of all labour theorists leads many writers to suppose that he shares, or at any rate should have shared, this conclusion; but as we shall see, it is an important part of Macpherson's case that Locke never intended such a limitation at all. The two initial limitations are transcended by the invention of money. They are not broken or cast aside; rather, the sort of conditions under which they are applicable no longer obtain. The invention of money is seen by Locke as the discovery of:

> . . . some lasting thing that Men might keep without spoiling, and that by mutual consent Men would take in exchange for the truly useful, but perishable Supports of Life.[12]

Although a man may by purchase acquire more land than he can use the immediate product of, he still leaves enough and as good for other men. It is true that this is not enough *land* and as good as that appropriated—though Locke seems at times to want to argue that even this is true—but rather that the standard of living is at least as good as before for everyone else.[13] That is, even when all the land is appropriated, the

[9] Secs. 27, 33, 35.
[10] Secs, 31, 37, 38, 46.
[11] e.g. at sec. 27.
[12] Sec. 47.
[13] Secs. 37, 41.

general standard of living is improved for everyone, even for the landless, because the invention of money has enabled the rational capitalist
to apply his skills and labour to land and raw material that were
formerly of little or no value to mankind. Locke puts a good deal of
stress on this:

> For I aske whether in the wild woods and uncultivated wast of America left
> to Nature, without any improvement, tillage or husbandry, a thousand acres
> will yield the needy and wretched inhabitants as many conveniences of life
> as ten acres of equally fertile land doe in Devonshire where they are well
> cultivated.[14]

Besides this transcending of the sufficiency limitation, there is now no
risk of infringing the *spoliation limitation*. For money does not decay,
so however much of it a man has, he has no fears of it perishing
uselessly in his possession. A man may heap up gold and silver *ad
infinitum*:

> . . . he might heap up as much of these durable things as he pleased; the
> exceeding of the bounds of his just Property not lying in the largeness of
> his Possession, but the perishing of anything uselessly in it.[15]

As for the third limitation, Locke never meant it to hold. The crucial
point about Locke's calling labour a form of property is not that it is a
peculiar and sacred form of property, but that being property it is
alienable; in the state of nature as elsewhere, men must be supposed
free to exchange their labour for subsistence or for a wage. (Indeed
they must, if Locke's fantasy of a pre-political market economy is to
make any sense.) In his support Macpherson quotes Locke's equation
of 'my' labour with the labour of my servant. The passage runs:

> Thus the Grass my Horse has bit; the Turfs my Servant has cut; and the
> Ore I have digg'd in any place where I have a right to them in common
> with others, become my *Property*, without the assignation or consent of
> anybody. The *labour* that was mine, removing them out of that common
> state they were in, hath *fixed* my *Property* in them.[16]

The only meaning that such a passage will bear indicates that Locke
never doubted that one man could appropriate the labour of another
and thus become the owner of it. 'My' labour includes the labour of

[14] Sec. 37.
[15] Sec. 46.
[16] Sec. 28.

anyone I employ; hence the requirement that we mix 'our' labour with whatever we appropriate imposes no limits on the right to appropriate.

Given that it is morally excellent to accumulate property, whether consumable or durable, but particularly the latter, and given that the invention of money enables such accumulation to go on indefinitely, certain consequences for Locke's political theory may be drawn. Macpherson not only goes on to draw them, but holds that Locke drew them too, and, further that Locke regarded them as the most important parts of his theory. The first is that Locke's wide definition of property as: 'Lives, Liberties, and Estates, which I call by the general Name Property'[17] is not the one usually adhered to, and is not the one involved in the crucial sections of the *Second Treatise* dealing with the limits on the authority of any government and with the right of the people to rebel against governments which they find oppressive.[18] In these passages, says Macpherson, 'property' means what we normally mean by the term, and refers particularly to property in fixed capital goods. From this it follows that 'the people' to whom Locke entrusts the right of rebellion cannot be the whole population, but must be the propertied classes only. The grounds of revolt are comprised under the heading of the government failing to preserve the property of its citizens; since very few people have any property, only this small number have any right to rebel. Labourers without property are in any case not fully rational—as demonstrated by the fact that they have no property—and therefore have no claim to full membership of civil society.

> While the labouring class is a necessary part of the nation its members are not in fact full members of the body politic and have no claim to be so . . . Whether by their own fault or not, members of the labouring class did not have, could not be expected to have, and were not entitled to have full membership in political society.[19]

As something less than full members of political society, they are objects of administration rather than citizens. This part of Macpherson's case is a crucial one, and my criticism of Macpherson's interpretation of Locke is largely concerned with this part of his account. An added merit Macpherson claims for his account is that it disposes of such riddles as Locke's basing obligation upon consent. If 'the people' are in fact the propertied classes, then they will readily give their

---

[17] Sec. 124.
[18] Macpherson pp. 198, 230–1, 247–50
[19] Macpherson pp. 221, 227.

consent to whatever the legislative enacts, since what it enacts will always be in their class-interest, and the interest of the class against the rest of society is more vital to each member of it than is his own interest against other members of his class. The state has thus become a committee for managing the common interests of bourgeoisie. Naturally this also solves the clash between the individualist and collectivist elements in Locke's thought. To behave as an extreme individualist is to behave as a successful capitalist, and this is to achieve moral excellence; it is however a form of moral excellence only possible at the expense of those against whom one competes successfully, and of those whose labour one uses to enrich oneself. Hence what is needed by the individualist is a strong government which will hold the ring for their competition. Its strength is no threat to them, since it is a blatant instrument of class-rule; the tough capitalist does not require protection from his fellows.

The individuals who have the means to realize their personalities (that is, the propertied) do not need to reserve any rights as against civil society, since civil society is constructed by and for them, and run by and for them.[20]

The propertied class has a coherent, cohesive interest in maintaining its position *vis à vis* the labouring classes. Individual rights thus disappear; the labouring classes have none, the propertied class needs none. Similarly the oft noted analogy between Locke's civil society and a joint-stock company takes on a new aspect. Locke

. . . would have no difficulty in thinking of the state as a joint-stock company of owners whose majority decision binds not only themselves, but also their employees.[21]

The only shareholders in the firm are the board of directors. The workers are employed to maximize the wealth of the firm, but have no say in the running of the company. Thus the domination of the state by the rising bourgeoisie is complete; its goals are their goals; its machinery is their machinery; its decisions are their decisions. Their power over the labouring proletariat is absolute, and it is rightly so.

II

Macpherson supports this account of the ideological Locke with a good deal of quotation from the *Second Treatise;* but it will be

---

[20] Macpherson p. 256.
[21] Macpherson p. 251.

appreciated by anyone familiar with that work and the variety of interpretation to which it has given rise, that no conclusive argument emerges from these quotations alone. The establishing of Locke as a capitalist lackey rests heavily, therefore, on his economic writings, where his attitude to the labouring poor, and even more to the unemployed, is indubitably severe. Similarly Locke's disparagement of the rationality of the poor is drawn from the *Reasonableness of Christianity*. In the light of a theory drawn from these sources it is not difficult to put the appropriate gloss on the ambiguous passages of the *Second Treatise*. (My objections to Macpherson are all based on the *un*ambiguous passages to which he pays less careful attention, I fear.) About these outside sources I am sceptical. For one thing they cover a period of forty years, and one may doubt both Locke's consistency over that period and his remaining interested in precisely the same problems for so long. For a second thing, the *Reasonableness of Christianity* was largely written to point out that the detailed disputes of the sects were beyond the scope of *anybody's* reason, and its moral hardly seems to be that the working class is peculiarly irrational. It may be an ungracious response to so exciting an account as Macpherson's, but the impression made by his welding together of all his disparate evidence into a tough, lucid, and consistent theory is that of an interpretative *tour de force* rather than of a natural or convincing account of Locke.

Confining ourselves to the *Second Treatise*, there is ample room for doubt about Macpherson's account, and some plainly unambiguous statements by Locke that flatly contradict it. On the issue of rationality, for example, it is true that this is Locke's basis for knowledge of the moral law and hence the basis for being able to obey it. But it is quite incredible that Locke intends us to believe it is the property of one class only, or that he thinks it is chiefly displayed in the acquisition of capital goods. It is stated explicitly by Locke that very nearly all men are rational enough to know what the Law of Nature requires of them, though most men are little enough inclined always to obey it:

> The *State of Nature* has a Law of Nature to govern it, which obliges everyone; and Reason which is that Law teaches all mankind who will but consult it. . . .[22]

The problem is not that some people have not the ability to know what the Law requires of them, but that they will not take the trouble to think that they are morally obliged to do, or if they do take that

[22] Sec. 6 cf. 12 &c.

trouble they will not take the trouble to do what they are morally obliged to. The reason, in general, why the Law of Nature is not enough is human selfishness and not human intelligence. In fact the only qualification Locke places on the general possession of rationality is that of age or mental defect:

. . . we are born Free, as we are born Rational; not that we have actually the exercise of either; Age that brings one, brings with it the other too.[23]

The only persons other than the young who are not qualified by rationality are

Lunaticks and Ideots . . . Madmen[24]

who hardly seem to be coextensive with the whole class of the labouring poor whom Locke is said to have written off as non-rational. Moreover, this statement by Locke comes only one chapter after the account of property rights in which the erosion of the rationality of the propertyless is supposed to have occurred. The total absence of any sign that Locke was sliding into the doctrine which is said to be his considered opinion leaves us with no grounds for supposing that the mere absence of property in the sense of capital goods is sufficient to deny citizenship to persons who, by all normal tests, are sane and rational when they reach years of discretion.

Moreover, there is a good deal of confusion in Macpherson's account of what is supposed by Locke to be the distinctively rational feature about capitalist accumulation. There is initially a good deal of confusion in Locke too, but Macpherson does not so much clear this up as ignore it in favour of a doctrine which he attributes to Locke, apparently for no better cause than that it is the doctrine which a moralizing capitalist ought to have held. The only consistent line for Locke to take is fairly simple, and the elements of it are at least hidden in the account of property rights he does give. The Will of God, which he identifies with the Law of Nature and the demands of Reason, requires all men to be preserved as far as possible. The man who appropriates land, employs his skill upon it, and thus enriches mankind, is thereby obeying the demands of reason, that is, he is being rational. This is Locke's argument in a number of places. He refers

[23] Sec. 61.
[24] Sec. 60.

initially to the right that each man has of preserving all mankind[25]—a 'right' which is better termed a duty. He argues that the man who encloses land and works it confers a benefit upon mankind; almost everything required for a civilized existence is due to the skill and effort which men have lavished upon the raw materials supplied by nature. In one passage he begins with the assertion:

> I think it will be but a very modest Computation to say, that of the *Products* of the Earth useful to the Life of Man nine out of ten are the *effects of Labour*.[26]

Just how modest he thinks this computation to be appears soon enough:

> . . . nay, if we will rightly estimate things as they come to our use, and cast up the several Expences about them, what in them is purely owing to *Nature*, and what to *labour*, we shall find, that in most of them ninety-nine out of one hundred are wholly to be put on the account of *labour*.[27]

And a moment later the proportion becomes 999 parts in 1,000.[28] The invention of money allows this process to be carried to the lengths typical of a developed economy. Thus the labourer, along with society generally, benefits from the activities of the capitalists. And this is the rationale of capitalism. But, what is the incentive for the capitalist himself? According to Macpherson, Locke holds that capitalists develop their personalities in capitalism; but Locke says nothing of the sort, and in any case, it is both an unconvincing and vacuous account of the matter. What does it amount to beyond the assertion that people who want to become capitalists gratify their wish if they do become capitalists? Locke in fact is confused. At one point he suggests that nothing more than a fanciful liking for gold is at the bottom of it—but the rationality of piling up prettily coloured stones and metals is not clear. The value of money, of course, is a fancy value not in the sense of being a *fanciful* value, but in the sense of being an agreed or conventional value. But Locke does sometimes equate this with having no value at all. When he refuses to allow the conqueror the right to the conquered's territory, he excludes money thus:

[25] e.g. sec. 11.
[26] Sec. 40.
[27] Sec. 40.
[28] Sec. 43.

For as to Money, and such Riches and Treasure taken away, these are none of Natures Goods, they have but a Phantastical imaginary value: Nature has put no such upon them . . .[29]

This clearly confuses conventional value and no value at all. The explanation of the good sense of capitalism that Locke hints at elsewhere, which makes a sound case, had three elements in it. The first is that men have come to have more wants than nature gave them; they desire more than they absolutely need; clearly the day labourer living at English subsistence level is much better off than the Indian king living at a high standard for a savage; a rational man will clearly join in this better consumption—an explanation of the inducement to become a capitalist which Macpherson rejects, but which makes good sense. But, on occasion Locke identifies the desire of having more than we need with simple greed, and suggests that the pre-monetary state of nature was a Golden Age.[30] In which case, the capitalist is not merely not rational, not morally excellent, but positively corrupt. (Macpherson's defence[31] that the condemnation of greed applies not to the capitalist but to the property-less who covet the capitalists' goods is clever, but is impossible to reconcile what Locke says about the earliest governments ruling a simple society. It is the whole state of society, not that of a single class which Locke commends or disapproves, and he clearly places the arrival of greed at the time of the invention of money.)[32] The second element is that we have already discussed, namely the argument that the capitalist is morally bound to promote the well-being of society; and Locke tends—as we noted in the case where he terms a duty a 'right'—to equate being bound by reason with wanting to do what reason tells one. So for Locke doing what is right can be something the capitalist gets out of being a capitalist. The third element is Locke's suggestion that a man will want to provide for other people to whom he feels an obligation or perhaps for those to whom he simply wants to give his goods. Giving away is a recognized form of use.[33] Of these three elements, only the first is a genuine prudential consideration which would allow us to say that the capitalist was being rational in the prudential sense rather than in the moral sense. It is plainly the account which Locke ought to have taken to match his conventionalist account of money. For if money has a conventional

[29] Sec. 184 cf. sec. 46.
[30] Sec. 111.
[31] Macpherson pp. 236–7.
[32] Sec. 108.
[33] Sec. 46.

value within some society or other, then the whole point of getting rich is to be able to share the advantages of that society's economy to an increased extent. It seems that Macpherson confuses further what Locke confuses sufficiently. The only consistent line to be found in Locke is that capitalism is rational—morally—because it is a step to the betterment of society, and that being a capitalist is rational—prudentially—because it enables one to enjoy a greater share of the betterment. A man's share in the greater social product is both his incentive and his reward. But so simple a doctrine as this is far indeed from fulfilling the requirements of Macpherson's theory.

This becomes clearer when we examine Macpherson's curious assertion that property rights are absolute because labour rights are so. The labour theory of proprietorship has been much misunderstood by Macpherson. It begins not as a theory of proprietorship but as theory of identification.[34] Locke says of the diet of the Indian:

> The Fruit, or Venison, which nourishes the wild *Indian*, who knows no Inclosure, and is still a Tenant in common, must be his, and so his, i.e. a part of him, that another can no longer have any right to it, before it can do him any good for the support of his Life.[35]

But the sense in which food must belong to a man before it can do him any good is a biological one—namely he has to eat it; and the sense in which an Indian's nourishment is *his* is a logical one—namely that we can only identify nourishment by identifying the man nourished. This is not to talk of rights at all, and particularly not to talk of absolute rights. It is a very dangerous way of talking, for it swiftly confuses the 'his' of identification with the 'his' of ownership or rightful possession. Thus, there is a perfectly good sense in which: 'The *Labour* of his Body, and the *Work* of his Hands we may say, are properly his.[36] But this sense needs elucidating. In one sense it is bound to be 'his', as it is a truth of logic that only *he* can do *his* labouring, and in this sense, whomever he labours for, it is still 'his' labour. But this does not establish that the only person entitled to benefit from his labour is himself. It is moreover impossible to reconcile Locke's concern for the rights of wives and children with the right to be absolutely selfish which Macpherson ascribes to Locke's natural man. The confusion may be as much Locke's fault as anyone's, but it is fair to point out

[34] See J. P. Day, *Philosophical Quarterly*, April 1964.
[35] Sec. 26.
[36] Sec. 27.

that Locke never talks of an 'absolute' right to anything at all. Customarily accepted moral obligations are not mentioned—or not often —but this might well be because Locke took them for granted, not because he did not accept them. Locke's concern after all was to defend men against royal force and robbery, and this is not a category which includes the demands of friends and family. The point of Locke's initial account of the right to goods given by labour is surely negative. He is faced with the question of how undifferentiated goods become the exclusive property of some one man; and the answer is that where there is plenty for everyone, acquisition and ownership need not be distinguished. If a man acquires something without breaking the laws of nature in the manner of his acquiring it, that is enough. The answer to the question 'Who has it?' serves as the answer to the question 'Who has it?'. Macpherson's emphasis on the absence of obligation to society is odd in view of the fact that at this point the conditions which create social ties do not exist at all; and the minimal obligation of leaving enough and as good for whomever may chance along is surely some sort of obligation, while obligations to one's family presumably exist at this rudimentary stage too. And Locke says clearly enough that when a man enters society he has his social title to his goods on society's terms[37]—a pre-echo of Rousseau. This after all is Locke's consistent line; we enter society to protect our property, so we must be prepared to contribute our fair share of whatever is required for this defence, and society must judge what it needs for the successful performance of its functions. If property includes life, limb, liberty, and possessions, then some pay taxes, but all forgo their natural liberty, and all are liable for the defence of the country from enemies external and internal.[38]

If we are correct in arguing that talk of 'absolute' property is seriously misleading and that no sort of absolute ownership is involved in either life, liberty or goods, on all of which there can be claims, then there seems less reason than ever to suppose that Locke restricts the meaning of 'property' to fixed property in goods, or to suppose that he is engaged in an attempt to deprive the proletariat of all political rights for the benefit of the employing classes. The only essential characteristic that property possesses is that property is that of which a man cannot be deprived without his consent; for example, Locke says of the rights of the conquered under the conqueror:

[37] Sec. 120.
[38] Secs. 128–30.

. . . whatsoever he grants them, they have so far as it is granted, *property* in. The nature whereof is, that *without a Man's own consent* it *cannot be taken from him*.[39]

And elsewhere, it is the absence of this characteristic that removes a possession from the position of actually being a man's property:

For I have truly no *Property* in that, which another can by right, take from me, when he pleases, against my consent.[40]

This characteristic applies for Locke to all goods both bodily and mental, save one's own life, which one cannot dispose of by contract, but which one can lose the right to by a sufficient breach of the natural law. It is significant that Macpherson's view of the power exercised over the property-less is that of Locke; it is despotic power, absolute and arbitrary, a power which Locke explicitly contrasts with political power. And it is crucially important to notice that the only case of despotic power allowed by Locke, and hence by inference the only case he allows of a man without property, is power over the renegade against reason and society:

. . . *Despotical Power* is an absolute, arbitrary power one man has over another, to take away his life, whenever he pleases. This is a power, which neither nature gives . . . nor compact can convey . . . but it is *the effect only of forfeiture*, which the aggressor makes of his own life, when he puts himself into the state of war with another.[41]

Of political power he says in the next paragraph:

(By *Property* I must be understood here, as in other places, to mean that property which men have in their persons as well as goods.) *Voluntary Agreement gives . . . Political Power to Governours* for the benefit of their subjects, to secure them in the possession and use of their properties.[42]

And this power is immediately contrasted with power over the property-less:

And *Forfeiture* gives the third, *Despotical Power to Lords* for their own benefit, over those who are stripp'd of all property.[43]

[39] Sec. 195.
[40] Sec. 138.
[41] Sec. 172.
[42] Sec. 173.
[43] Sec. 173.

And finally he sums up:

Paternal Power is only where minority makes the child incapable to manage his property; *Political* where men have property in their own disposal; and *Despotical* over such as have no property at all.[44]

This seems to me conclusive enough against Macpherson's thesis that 'property' is to be read as if it referred only to property in goods. An obvious consequence, however, that we must draw is that if we accept Locke's wide reading of property as *bona civilia,* or 'life, liberty, health, and indolency of body; and the possession of outward things such as money, lands, houses, furniture, and the like',[45] then it is clear that we must accept the whole population who have reached years of discretion as being the 'people' for the purposes of entrusting them with the right of revolution. That Locke did so is shown clearly by what he considers as a possible objection to his doctrine:

To this perhaps it will be said, that the people being ignorant, and always discontented, to lay the foundation of Government in the unsteady opinion, and uncertain humour of the people, is to expose it to certain ruine.[46]

His reply does not matter: what is important is how this contradicts Macpherson's picture of Locke. Locke is hardly likely to think it a plausible criticism of the rising capitalists that they are ignorant or unsteady of opinion or uncertain of humour. One verbal point that might lead one into accepting Macpherson's account is Locke's talk of 'deputies' and 'representatives'; it is easy enough to slip into thinking that this involves electing M.P.s—and of course no-one suggests that Locke is advocating universal suffrage. But, if we recall that Locke counts a monarch, ruling without a council, or a permanent oligarchy, as legislatives in precisely the same sense as the English King-in-Parliament is a legislative, it becomes clear that to be represented is not necessarily to have voted.[47] Macpherson may still be willing to argue that the labourer is not a 'full member' of civil society—but the trouble here is that Locke talks only of members, and never distinguishes between full and any other sort of membership. The passage Macpherson rests his case on is an oddity, and is anyway concerned

[44] Sec. 174.
[45] Laslett's note to sec. 3.
[46] Sec. 223.
[47] Sec. 138.

with distinguishing the status of foreigners residing in a country from that of genuine subjects:

> And thus we see, that *Foreigners,* by living all their lives under another Government, and enjoying the priviledges and protection of it, though they are bound, even in conscience, to submit to its administration, as far forth as any Denison; yet do not hereby come to be *Subjects or Members of that Commonwealth.* Nothing can make any man so, but his actually entering into it by positive engagement, and express promise and compact.[48]

Here it is the foreigner who is being contrasted with the member or subject; Macpherson's contrast is between the labourer who is a subject but not a member, and the propertied man who is both, a contrast of which the text is innocent. The obligation that the labourer and the foreigner incur, they incur along with the capitalist, for they have all given their tacit consent by enjoying property:

> . . . whether this his possession be of land to him and his heirs for ever, or a lodging only for a week; or whether it be barely travelling freely on the highway.[49]

If this puts the labourer on a level with the foreigner it does so only by putting him on a level with his employer too. Locke never solves the problem of why a man's first country is thought to be his only country, but it is surely implausible to suggest that he anticipated Marx in holding that the proletarian has no country, only a class. It would be a foolish doctrine for Locke to hold, since it would have involved him in releasing labourers from the obligation to defend their country against external enemies, and would have meant that they could not be held guilty of such crimes as treason. We cannot but conclude that if labourers can be said to have a property—and we have seen no reason why they cannot be—then they are members of civil society. They receive benefits and accept corresponding obligations. They may pay no taxes, but they lend their labour and their strength to the defence of their society against enemies internal and external:

> . . . the *Power of Punishing* he wholly *gives up,* and engages his natural force (which he might before imploy in the execution of the Law of Nature, by his own single Authority, as he thought fit) to assist the executive power of his society, as the law thereof shall require.[50]

[48] Sec. 122.
[49] Sec. 119.
[50] Sec. 130 cf. 136.

Men allow society to regulate their lives, their liberties and their possessions; all who have need of protection for any of these things can receive it from civil society and thereby become obliged by its rules. The state exists not for a class but for all who are willing and able to use it on equitable terms.

III

Although Macpherson's theory about Locke's doctrine is thus falsified in so many details, it still presents a challenge to any critic. For its overall coherence and interest is extremely impressive, even though its foundations are shaky; and some of the detail—for example the exposition of Locke's defence of unequal property rights—is superior to anything yet produced on Locke. All discounting made of the ideological overtones which Macpherson hears in every word of Locke, the force of Macpherson's account challenges one to produce some alternative picture that fits the text better than his, but which takes notice of what is most valuable in his account. Let us then agree that the chapter *Of Property* is intended to justify the achievement of the capitalist, and the reward he reaps. As we argued above, the simplest argument for this is based on God's will that all mankind should flourish. Given fair distribution, the greatest social product is the will of God, and the dictate of reason. Locke never argues explicitly that the distribution is fair, though the elements of the argument required are there. They lie in the insistence that even the worst off in modern society is better off than he would be outside it, a thesis backed up by the ubiquitous American Indian; these latter it will be remembered:

. . . have not one hundredth part of the Conveniences we enjoy: And a King of a large and fruitful Territory there feeds, lodges and is clad worse than a day Labourer in *England*.[51]

And they lie too in the suggestion that it is the superior ability and greater efforts of the capitalist that leads to his greater wealth:

And as different degrees of Industry were apt to give Men Possessions in different proportions, so this *Invention of Money* gave them the opportunity to continue and enlarge them.[52]

[51] Sec. 41.
[52] Sec. 48.

And perhaps, finally, in the suggestion that even now there is some surplus land left:

in some inland, vacant places of America.[53]

Thus, the capitalist is worthy of his profit; that he is worthy of all his profit Locke does not argue; perhaps his *laissez-faire* inclinations were not so strong that he thought it was true; perhaps they were so strong that he thought it needed no proving. The basic point, however, is simple enough; since all men have profited by entering a market society, there is no cause for complaint if some men have done better than others.

But, here we part company with Macpherson. In Macpherson's account, Locke now proceeds to pile political oppression on top of inequality of possessions. A more convincing picture is that of Locke moving from the negative point that the labourer and the capitalist were not at odds to the positive task of showing that they have a shared interest, a common ground of political obligation, and a common right to see to the maintenance of their interests. It is indubitable that both are bound by the law; therefore the law must give something to them both, in return for which they are bound to obey it. And it is this something which Locke calls:

. . . the Preservation of their Property[54]

or else

. . . the mutual *Preservation* of their *Lives, Liberties and Estates* which I call by the general Name, Property.[55]

A common interest requires one term to describe it, even though the most disparate things come as a result to shelter under the name of 'property'. All the inhabitants of a well-governed and well-organized country benefit from its government—even resident foreigners—so they all have a share in something; and whatever it is that they have a share in Locke calls property. Peace and security are also said by Locke to be the ends of government; men enter civil society:

[53] Sec. 36.
[54] Sec. 124.
[55] Sec. 123.

. . . by *stated Rules* of Right and Property to secure their Peace and Quiet.[56]

All men require peace and security to lead tolerable lives, so all men have so much property as requires government for its preservation. It is, of course, odd to talk of all the things that society protects as property, but the effect is surely not that of setting up a bourgeois dictatorship so much as finding some common interest shared by both the proletarian and the bourgeois in a state which must often have seemed to give nothing save to those who were rich and powerful enough to need nothing from it. And the importance of giving the proletariat and the bourgeoisie a common interest is surely that their interests are opposed to absolute monarchy; nothing could be clearer than that the target of the *Second Treatise* is not the peaceful and docile proletariat, but the doctrine that a monarch has an absolute, and more particularly an arbitrary, power over his subjects. This is a recurring theme of the whole treatise, which might indeed have been subtitled a treatise against arbitrariness and in favour of relevance in political power. A large part of the chapter *Of the Dissolution of Government* is a defence of regicide as a last measure against a king who claims to have an absolute and arbitrary authority over his people.[57] Despite occasionally light-hearted manner in which he discusses the question of how we are to join reverence with a knock on the head, Locke commits himself to views which abundantly explain why he did not wish to be known as the author of the work during the lifetime of James II. Locke's bitterest attacks are always on absolute monarchy, as when he says:

Hence it is evident that *Absolute Monarchy*, which by some men is counted the only Government in the world, is indeed *inconsistent with Civil Society*.[58]

or that:

Absolute, arbitrary power, or governing without *settled standing Laws*, can neither of them consist with the ends of society and government.[59]

or that:

[56] Sec. 137.
[57] Secs. 232–9.
[58] Sec. 90.
[59] Sec. 137.

Absolute Dominion, however placed, is so far from being one kind of civil society, that it is as incompatible with it, as slavery is with property.[60]

It seems quite incredible that anyone should not take it as an attack on the pretensions made by James II (or those which he was suspected of being about to make) to the position of a recipient of divinely granted power, and thus to freedom from all human law and control. Locke's target is arbitrariness rather than absoluteness; he goes into some detail about martial law, which allows summary execution for disobedience even to lethally dangerous orders, but which will not allow a general to touch one penny of a soldier's goods; the reason given by Locke is that this is:

Because such a blind Obedience is necessary to that end for which the Commander has his Power, *viz* the preservation of the rest; but the disposing of his Goods has nothing to do with it.[61]

Locke generalizes the argument that authority is limited in its scope to what is necessary to secure the ends for which the authority is set up to cover the case of parliament, the monarch and any other sort of authority. All rights are limited by the ends they are meant to secure, and the right to our obedience vested in our rulers is in exactly the same case. Royal authority, in other words, depends not on the person of the monarch, but on the good of the society. The quarrel is not between bourgeoisie and proletariat, but between king and people. No doubt the people are but rarely justified in revolution; but there is no question that they have the right to rebel *in extremis.*

    Even on this reading of Locke, his theory is still a bourgeois one. It is beyond doubt a bourgeois mind which envisages all rights as property rights; it is also, more importantly for the political philosopher, a perceptive sort of confusion that leads to such an identification. For 'property' is not an inapt general name for the class or rights and obligations that enter into social theory—quasi-contractual rights and duties as they are. For in many ways property rights, in the ordinary sense of 'property', are paradigms of the rights that are exchanged and protected by contract. But only a bourgeois mind could fail to see that they are paradigmatic rather with respect to procedure than with respect to the importance of the ethical values involved. They are paradigmatically contractual, but they are not the most

[60] Sec. 174.
[61] Sec. 139.

important contractual rights. But this still goes no way towards justifying Macpherson's attributing to Locke a ruthless, dictatorial programme of class-domination. In the joint-stock company that is Locke's state, all men are shareholders. Some men hold shares of life, liberty, peace, and quiet alone, while others hold shares of estate as well; these latter may receive more of the benefits and play a greater part in the running of the state, but there is no reason to suppose that in the eyes of God or Nature (or even in the eyes of John Locke) their shares have a peculiar importance. Few or no practical conclusions follow readily from Locke's account of political obligation; Macpherson's conclusions follow even less readily than the more egalitarian and humane ones that have been drawn in the past.

LOCKE ON PROPERTY*

J. P. Day

1. INTRODUCTION

The object of this essay is to examine Locke's justification of private property. But before proceeding to the examination, I have two preliminary points to make about its scope. On the one hand, its scope is wide, for the reason that Locke intends his justification to apply to utilities of all kinds. We shall see that Locke's thesis is that every man has a right to own that which he has mixed his labour with; for which reason I call his doctrine his Labour Theory of Property (Sec. 2). Locke's examples of such mixing of labour include making a loaf of bread, picking an apple from a wild apple-tree, and cultivating a piece of hitherto virgin land. The last point calls for special notice. For many writers on property-rights draw a sharp distinction between property in artefacts on the one hand and property in the earth and its natural products on the other, and maintain that private property in these two sorts of utilities requires different justifications. Mill, for instance, agrees with Locke that the foundation of the former property-right is "the right of producers to what they themselves have produced", but maintains that this principle cannot justify private property in land since "no man made the land". By contrast, Locke contends that this principle does justify private property in land as well as in artefacts because working land is just one way of mixing labour with something. Hence, "As much land as a man tills, plants, improves, cultivates, and can use the product of, so much is his property. He by his labour does as it were enclose it from the common."[1]

On the other hand, the scope of the essay is restricted inasmuch as we shall consider no justification of private property other than Locke's. For more than two centuries the justification most often

---

* Reprinted with minor alterations from the *Philosophical Quarterly*, Vol. 16 (1966), 207–221, by permission of the editor and author.
[1] J. Locke, *Second Treatise of Government*, 1690, ch. 5, sec. 32: J. S. Mill, *Principles of Political Economy*, 7th ed., 1871, bk. 2, ch. 1, sec. 1; ch. 2, sec. 6.

given, e.g. by Mill, has been a very different one, namely, the Utilitarian. It was in 1751 that Hume asked: "Who sees not . . . that whatever is produced or improved by a man's art or industry ought, for ever, to be secured to him, in order to give encouragement to such *useful* habits and accomplishments?"[2] In 1802, however, Bentham pointed out that "of two individuals . . . he that has the most wealth has the greatest chance of happiness", but that "the excess in happiness of the richer will not be so great as the excess of his wealth".[3] In other words, that the maximization of total utility or happiness requires equal distribution of wealth on account of D. Bernoulli's Law of Diminishing Utility of 1738.[4] Hence the Utilitarian dilemma. On the one hand, Bernoulli's law requires equal distribution of wealth; on the other hand, Hume's principle sanctions unequal distribution of wealth, since according to it the man who produces more wealth ought of course to have more wealth than the man who produces less wealth. The solution adopted by most Utilitarians was to subordinate Bernoulli's law to Hume's principle, thereby in effect treating the distribution of wealth as secondary to, and as a means to, the production of wealth. Here, clearly, is a question of the greatest practical importance. In particular, is Hume's principle strictly true? Or is it not possible to devise social arrangements which will provide sufficient inducements to production, but which will distribute wealth, not according to "desert", but according to some ethically superior principle, such as equality or need? However, we shall not be concerned with this great question on the present occasion.

Notwithstanding that Locke's theory has thus long been superseded by the Utilitarian one, its philosophical interest and historical significance amply warrant a critical consideration of it. I touch on its historical significance later (Sec. 5). I hope that the rest of this essay will bring out its philosophical interest.

2. EXPOSITION

Locke summarizes his justification of private property in the following famous passage:

[2] D. Hume, *An Enquiry concerning the Principles of Morals*, 1751, sec. 3, pt. 2.

[3] J. Bentham, *Principles of the Civil Code*, ed. Dumont, 1802, ch. 6. Cp. Hume, *l.c.*

[4] D. Bernoulli, *Specimen Theoriae Novae de Mensura Sortis*, 1738.

Though the earth and all inferior creatures be common to all men, yet every man has a property in his own person; this nobody has any right to but himself. The labour of his body and the work of his hands we may say are properly his. Whatsoever, then, he removes out of the state that nature hath provided and left it in, he hath mixed his labour with, and joined to it something that is his own, and thereby makes it his property. It being by him removed from the common state nature placed it in, it hath by this labour something annexed to it that excludes the common right of other men. For this labour being the questionable property of the labourer, no man but he can have a right to what that is once joined to, at least where there is enough and as good left in common for others.[5]

The gist of this argument may be rendered:

(1) Every man has a right to own his person
∴(2) Every man has a right to own the labour of his person
∴(3) Every man has a right to own that which he has mixed the labour of his person with.

By *right* Locke clearly intends *moral right*, not *legal right*. Plainly, we have here two distinct arguments, first from (1) to (2), and then from (2) to (3). I shall discuss them separately, beginning with the second one.

3. CRITICISM

(a) *My Work.* The first criticism of Locke's second argument is that it is invalid, since it is possible to accept proposition (2) but reject proposition (3). For part of the meaning of (3) is that A has a moral right to the *exclusive* use of that which he has mixed his labour with. Yet this is questionable. Consider Locke's wild Indian, picking apples in some inland vacant place of America. Even though he has done all the picking, his wife and children surely have a moral right to use, i.e. eat, some of them?[6]

I suggest that the cause of Locke's mistake here is his failure to distinguish between two different senses of *work*.[7] He thinks, I believe, that the passage from (2) to (3) is scarcely an "inference" at all, but simply a move from *every man has a right to own his work* to

---

[5] Locke, *l.c.*, ch. 5, sec. 27.
[6] J. Plamenatz, *Man and Society*, London, 1963, vol. 1, pp. 244 f.
[7] For the reader's convenience, the different uses of *work* and *labour* distinguished in this essay are summarized in an appendix.

every man has a right to own his work, which looks irreproachable if uninteresting. But it is in fact fallacious because *work* does not mean the same thing in the two statements. In the former, $work_1$ means *working*, $labour_1$ or *labouring*. It is an activity. It is in this sense that we speak of, say, *Russell's labours*. In the latter, on the other hand, $work_3$ does not mean *working*. It is not an activity but an achievement, and we speak of *a work* rather than of plain *work*. It is in this sense that we talk of *defensive works* or *Russell's works*. $Works_3$ are related to but not identical with $works_1$. Russell's works are not identical with Russell's labours, but they are the result of them. The difference between $work_1$ and a $work_3$ can also be seen from the fact, which Locke himself stresses, that whereas $work_1$ is just $labour_1$, a $work_3$ is $labour_1$ mixed with land (i.e. natural resources).

We shall need to distinguish other different senses of *work* and of *labour*. When we speak of *the work of converting the heathen* or of *the labours of Hercules*, we mean *tasks*. Whereas $work_1$ is something which is being done and a $work_3$ is something which has been done, a $work_2$ is something which is to be done. Before he cleaned out the Augean stalls, the labours of Hercules were a $work_2$; while he was cleaning them they were $work_1$; and when he had cleaned them that was a $work_3$. Different again, but plainly germane to $work_1$, is the physicist's sense of *work*. In this case, work is measured by the product of a force and the distance through which it acts; thus, if A lifts a body weighing 10 pounds through a height of 10 feet, he is said to do 100 foot-pounds of $work_4$.

The essential point in this first criticism is to realize that there is no inconsistency in agreeing with Locke that A has a right to own his $work_1$, while yet disagreeing with him that A has a right to own the $work_3$ which is the effect of his $work_1$.

My second criticism of Locke's argument turns on the truth and significance of his proposition (2). It will be well to begin by simplifying the question. For a start, *A has a right to own the $work_1$ of his person* may be shortened to *A has a right to own his $work_1$*, since there is no difference between A's person and A or between this person and me. To say that A assaulted B's person is to say neither more nor less than that A assaulted B. Next, before considering this alleged right, it would be wise to concentrate on the statement *A owns his $work_1$ (or $labour_1$)*. There is perhaps a temptation to say that this statement is not merely true, but necessarily true, since to assert that A's $work_1$ is not his is to contradict oneself. But this contention may be objected to on two scores, namely, deputization and collaboration.

As to deputization. Suppose that the Indian is sick and that his son picks apples for him. Then B does A's work for him. But since B can thus do A's work, it is false that A's work is necessarily A's.

The reply to this objection will be clear in the light of the distinctions just drawn. When B does A's work for him, he discharges A's task (work$_2$) for him. He does not do A's labouring (work$_1$) for him. For B can no more do A's labouring for him than he can do his walking for him. That his son does not do the Indian's work$_1$ for him is also evident from the simple consideration that the Indian does no work$_1$. For, by the supposition, the Indian is sick and does no picking; it is his son who does that. But the son can no more do a deed which was never done than he can witness an occurrence which did not occur. This leaves indeed a residual difficulty about the sense in which B can discharge A's task for him, and to this I shall return shortly.

Now as to collaboration. Suppose that the Indian's son co-operates with him in picking apples. Then A and B do the same work. Hence, B can do A's work and conversely, so that it is false that A's work is necessarily his.

Co-operation differs from deputization in that in this case both A and B do work$_1$. What cannot be allowed to pass, however, is the assertion that in co-operative actions A and B do the *same* work. It will be objected that they do both do the same work$_1$ namely, picking apples. But it is only in a loose sense that they do even qualitatively the same work. For A will be picking one lot of apples from one tree, whereas B will be picking a different lot of apples from another tree; or, if from the same tree, then from a different part of it. Similarly, if A and B collaborate in sawing down a tree with a double saw, their work$_1$ will be qualitatively different, since A will be pulling the saw when B is pushing it, and conversely. *A fortiori*, they do not, because they cannot logically do numerically the same work$_1$. For the description, *the man who did X*, necessarily individuates some one person; in the case of co-operative actions the descriptions take the special forms *the man who did X with the help of B* and *the man who did X with the help of A*, which individuate A and B respectively.[8]

Co-operation nevertheless poses an insuperable difficulty for Locke's theory. An apple is normally picked by one man; but most artefacts are produced by several men collaborating in accordance with the Principle of the Division of Labour. But if a loaf is produced

[8] B. A. O. Williams, "Personal Identity and Individuation," *Aristotelian Society Proceedings*, London, March 1957, p. 233.

by the joint labours$_1$ of a farmer, a miller and a baker, to which of them, on Locke's theory, does it rightly appertain? His proposition (3) implies to all of them; but then, what are their rightful shares in it? The theory suggests the reply that this depends on the respective amounts of labour$_1$ which they have put into making it, and that this depends in turn on the respective lengths of time for which they have worked; so that if A has worked for twice as long as B or C, then their proper shares are one half, one quarter and one quarter of the loaf respectively. But this overlooks the important fact that labours$_1$ may differ in other respects besides duration, such as intensity or skill. If A has worked for twice as long as B or C, but B has worked somewhat harder than A or C, and C has laboured much more skilfully than A or B; what now are their rightful shares in the loaf? The problem is further complicated by the fact that, though it makes sense to say that A worked twice as long as B or C, it makes no sense to say that B worked twice as hard as A or C, or that C laboured thrice as skilfully as A or B. Locke's Labour Theory of Property is in fact unable to provide an answer to the problem posed.

The same difficulty also confronts his Labour Theory of Value. That Locke does hold such a theory is shown by his well-known assertion that ". . . it is labour . . . that puts the difference of value on everything . . ."[9]. Later patrons of this theory include Smith, Ricardo and Marx, all of whom maintain that the "value (in exchange)" of a commodity depends on the "amount of labour" embodied in it. But the above considerations bring out the practical impossibility of determining what the amount of labour embodied in any artefact actually is.

The refutation of the preceding objections from deputization and collaboration seems, then, to show that *A owns his work$_1$* is a necessary truth. Unfortunately, however, this proves too much for the purposes of Locke's argument. For if A must own his work$_1$, then Locke's proposition (2), *A has a right to own his work$_1$*, makes no sense. It is unintelligible to talk of A having a moral right to do X unless there is a possibility of him not doing X. It is not absurd to say that bachelors have a right to remain unmarried; but it is absurd to say that they have a right to be unmarried, since they can be no other.

I submit, however, that Locke's proposition (2) is open to a more

[9] Locke, *l.c.*, ch. 5, sec. 40: J. W. Gough, *John Locke's Political Philosophy*, Oxford, 1950, pp. 81 ff.: H. Clay, *Economics: an Introduction for the General Reader*, London, 1916, ch 14, secs. 1, 2.

fundamental criticism, namely, that it is illogical to speak of anyone *owning labour*$_1$ at all. But exception may be taken to this contention too.

To begin with, it is necessary to explain the meaning of *owns*. This question of the meaning of property is quite different from the question, or questions, of its justification. It is one thing to ask what powers over X are normally connoted by *A owns X*, but quite another thing to ask whether, and if so under what conditions, A is morally entitled to have some or all of these powers. In the standard or paradigm case of ownership, then, A owns X when he has the powers of exclusive use, including the destruction, of X, and when he has the power of alienating or transferring X.

It may be objected, therefore, that it makes perfectly good sense to speak of labour$_1$ being owned, since men do in fact exercise these powers over it. Locke, for one, thinks that this is so. He writes: ". . . the turfs my servant (= employee) has cut . . . become my property. . . . The labour that was mine removing them out of that common state they were in, hath fixed my property in them".[10] That is to say, what happens when A employs B is that B sells A his labour$_1$ for money, so that when B mixes that labour with land the product is rightfully A's by Locke's proposition (3). Since, therefore, B can sell his labour$_1$, he must first own it. Another of a similar persuasion is Marx, who maintains that, under Capitalism, "labour-power or capacity for labour" is a "commodity" which is bought and sold in the market.[11]

My replies to this objection are as follows. First, that one cannot talk significantly of *owning labour*$_1$. For labour$_1$, or labouring, is an activity, and although activities can be engaged in, performed or done, they cannot be owned. Secondly, that the objection rests on a confusion between labour$_1$ and yet another sense of *labour*, namely labour$_5$, which means, not *labouring*, but *labourers* or *workers*. This is the sense of *labour* in which we speak of *unskilled labour* and of *the Labour Party*. Now, labour$_5$ can indeed be owned. Nevertheless, only one kind of labour$_5$ actually is owned, namely slave-labour. True, A commonly speaks of *his* hireling or employee (cp. Locke's "my servant", above). But *his* does not in this case imply possession as it does in *A's slave*. For whereas slaves can be bought, sold, lent, given away and bequeathed, employees can only be hired and fired. The point is made

---

[10] Locke, *l.c.*, ch. 5, sec. 28.
[11] K. Marx, *Capital*, vol. 1, 1867, pt. 2, 4, sec. 3.

plain by considering other hired objects. If A hires or "rents" a TV set, he may well refer to it as *his* set, but he will not claim to own it.

We have seen that, according to Marx, that which an employee sells to his employer is not his activity of labouring (labour$_1$) but his power of labouring. But it is no more significant to talk of *owning a capacity for work$_1$* than it is to talk of *owning work$_1$*. Powers are used or disused; they are not owned or unowned. True, we say *A has an unlimited capacity for work;* but *has* does not here mean *owns*. Nor can powers, or activities either, be bought and sold. A can, logically, no more sell B his capacity for work$_1$ than he can lend him his understanding.

It remains to diagnose the causes of the erroneous belief that labour$_1$ can be owned. I suggest that there are two. First, as just said, confusing labour$_1$ which cannot be owned with labour$_5$ which can. Secondly, and of chief importance, thinking wrongly that the *his* in *A's* (i.e. *A his*) *labour$_1$* is possessive. Grammarians call *my, your, his,* etc. "possessive" adjectives. Sometimes, indeed often, they are so. But often, too, they are not; so that there is a constant danger of supposing that they are so when they are not. Take the following examples: *A's teeth, A's hare-lip, A's cold, A's golf, A's TV set* and *A's wife*. In the first four, the *his* cannot logically be possessive. In the fifth example, the *his* is usually possessive, but is not so if the set is hired. In the last case, the *his* is usually not possessive, but it is so in some primitive societies. Similarly with *A's work* and *A's labour*. In only two of the different uses of these expressions which I have distinguished can *his* be possessive. It is so in *Russell's works$_3$*, and Russell's property in these is in fact protected by copyright. It is so in *Pharaoh's labour$_5$* also, though not in *Ford's labour$_5$*. Nor is it so in *Jack's work$_4$*, in *Russell's labours$_1$*, or in *Russell's capacity for work$_1$*. *A's labour$_1$* is in fact just like *A's golf; A's work$_1$ is erratic* is an exact parallel of *A's golf is erratic*. *Mine, yours, ours,* etc. similarly have non-possessive as well as possessive uses. Illustrations of the former are *the Vice-Chancellor they refer to is ours* and *the foot you are standing on is mine*. There is perhaps a temptation to think that at any rate *my own, your own, his own,* etc. are always possessive; but such is not in fact the case. For contrast with the possessive use in *this house is my very own* and *a man may do what he will with his own* the following non-possessive uses: *I saw it with my own eyes, my own darling!* and *these paintings are all my own work*.

As for work$_2$, here also we use locutions which misleadingly suggest property. We talk of *the labours of Hercules,* and might talk of his *bequeathing* one of them which he failed to perform to his son. But the *of* in *the labours of Hercules* is not possessive, since tasks are not owned; they are rather undertaken or neglected, discharged or left incomplete. Nor can Hercules literally bequeath his task to his son, because the labours of Hercules are labours set for Hercules, and only Hercules can discharge a task appointed for Hercules to do. Consequently, although there is a sense in which his son can perform Hercules' task for him, we must recognize that the work$_2$ which his son performs is only qualitatively and not numerically the same as the work$_2$ which Hercules was to have performed. Again, we may speak of this generation of faithful *leaving* the work$_2$ of converting the heathen to the next generation. Here too, the word *leaving* misleadingly suggests a transmission of property. But the temptation to imagine this is not so strong as in Hercules' case, because the work of converting the heathen is not peculiarly this generation's task in the way that the labours of Hercules were set exclusively for Hercules. It is rather a task incumbent on all generations of the faithful. The case is similar with talk of *giving* work$_2$ to the unemployed. When A gives B work, he simply sets him some task, not necessarily or usually his own task.

As might be expected, what we have seen to be true of *his* is also true of *has* and of *of*. Lexicographers tell us that the primary meaning of *has* is *owns* or *possesses*. But there are also very numerous uses of this common word which have nothing to do with property. Many of them are uninteresting from the present point of view because there is no misleading grammatical resemblance to the possessive cases. Such are *A has arrived*, *A has to go* and *A had B shot*. But there are plenty of potentially confusing uses which are of the same grammatical form as the possessive use, which is *A has X*. Thus, compare with the (normally) possessive use *A has a car* the non-possessive use *A has no work$_2$*, *A has no capacity for work$_1$*, *A has no teeth*, *A has news*, *A had a game of golf* and the ambiguous use *A has a wife*. Similarly with *of*. Uninteresting, because not potentially misleading, uses are, e.g., *A is thinking of B*, *X is the cause of Y* and *X is made of Y*. But there are plenty of non-possessive uses of the same grammatical form as the possessive use, which is *the X of A*. Thus, contrast with the possessive *of* in *the works$_3$ of Russell* the non-possessive *of* in *the labours$_1$ of Russell*, *the labours$_2$ of Hercules*, *the King of the Hellenes*, *the travels of Marco Polo* and *the patience of Job*.

Finally, the answer to the natural question why some of the uses of *his*, *has* and *of* can, logically, be possessive whereas others cannot, is not difficult. We have seen that in standard employments *owns* implies powers of exclusive use, including destruction, and of alienation. But there is no point in talking about men having these powers over objects which cannot, in the nature of things, be used by others, or sold, given away or lent. Thus, B cannot use A's teeth because they form *part of* A; their use cannot but be exclusively A's. Hence likewise *A gave B his hand* is not (usually) a locution to be taken *au pied de la lettre;* nor did Mark Antony wish to be taken literally when he asked the Romans to lend him their ears. By contrast, B can borrow and use A's false teeth because they do not form part of A; which is why the *his* in *A's false teeth* is possessive. Hair, being easily detachable, is an interesting, because borderline, case. A can certainly present B with a lock for her locket, and if A is impatient or unscrupulous he may rape a lock of B's hair. Again, we say that A gave B his cold, but literally speaking this is a physical impossibility since A's cold is a condition of his body. Consequently, we are unwilling to allow that B can steal A's cold from him. Yet again, A's hare-lip is called a distinctive *property* of A. But this use of *property* has nothing to do with possession. It is necessary to distinguish X *is the property of A*, meaning X *appertains to A*, from X *is a property of A*, meaning X *characterizes A*. So too there are no actual or even imaginable states of affairs which can be described correctly and literally as A giving, selling or lending his labour$_1$ or his "labour-power" to B. Labour$_1$ and "labour-power" are strictly inalienable.

Whereas there is only one (standard) possessive use of *his, has* and *of*, there is not just one non-possessive use of these words, but a plurality of non-possessive uses. Thus, *A's work$_1$* means *work being done by A*, *A's work$_2$* means *work to be done by A*, *A's labour$_5$* means (in societies without slavery) *labour employed by A*, and so on. Again, *the King of the Hellenes* means *the King over the Hellenes*, *the patience of Job* means *the patience which is a property of Job*, and *A's heart* means *the heart which is a part of A*. Locke, however, confuses this last non-possessive use of *his* with the possessive use of it. For he advances the following auxiliary argument in support of his Labour Theory of Property:—When the Indian has digested the apple which he has picked and eaten, it is as much his as is his stomach. But since picking, eating and digesting it form a continuous process, the apple first became his, i.e. his property, when he picked it.[12] Locke's argu-

---

[12] Locke, *l.c.*, ch. 5, secs. 26, 28: Plamenatz, *l.c.*

ment is invalid, however, because he draws a conclusion of the form X *is the property of A* from a premiss of the form X *is a part of A*. For the sense of *his* in which both A's stomach and the digested apple are his is that they both form part of A. But, as we have seen in the preceding paragraph, X *is a part of A* is normally incompatible with X *is the property of A*. Notice, in this connexion, the difference in meaning between *A's body* and *A's person*. The former means *the body which is a part of A*, but the latter means simply *A*, as I pointed out earlier (Sec. 3). It is important not to misassimilate *A's person* to *A's body*, since if one does so one is bound to proceed to tease oneself with the unanswerable question, who is the A of whom A's person forms a part?

4. CRITICISM

(*b*) *Myself.* I turn now to Locke's first argument, that from proposition (1) to proposition (2) (Sec. 2). My first criticism of it is that proposition (1) is inconsistent with what Locke says elsewhere about suicide. His views on suicide and slavery are that in the State of Nature Man has no moral right to destroy himself, and that in political society he has no moral right to enslave himself. In the State of Nature, Man "has not liberty to destroy himself. . . . For men being all the workmanship of one omnipotent and infinitely wise Maker . . . they are his property, whose workmanship they are, made to last during his, not one another's pleasure". Under government, "a man not having the power of his own life cannot by compact, or his own consent, enslave himself to anyone. . . . Nobody can give more power than he has himself; and he that cannot take away his own life, cannot give another power over it".[13] According to the first quotation, God has a right to own Man because He made him. But this proposition, which is clearly a variant on proposition (3), is equally clearly incompatible with proposition (1).

One might well think that Locke is also inconsistent in saying that A has a right to own himself but no right to destroy or enslave himself, since a right to own X implies a right to destroy and alienate it. But this does not necessarily follow, for a reason which brings out an important point about the meaning of *owns*. In what I have called the standard or paradigm case of property, *A owns X* does indeed

---

[13] Locke, *l.c.*, ch. 2, sec. 6; ch. 4, sec. 23.

imply that A has powers of exclusive use, destruction and alienation over X. This is true when X is, e.g., a newspaper. However, we have to recognize that the concept of property is flexible, since A may still be called the owner of X when these conditions are by no means completely satisfied. Thus, suppose that A has a Rembrandt which he is legally compelled to allow the public to view at stated times, so that his use of it is not exclusive, and that he is legally prohibited from destroying it or selling it to would-be foreign purchasers. In spite of all this, the picture will still be legally his property. Accordingly, this objection to Locke is not decisive.

My second and main objection to Locke's first argument, however, is directed against the significance of speaking of owning oneself. Just as it makes no sense to speak of A's owning his labour₁, so, I submit, it makes no sense to speak of A owning himself. The reason is quite general, that *owns* or *possesses* and its converse *appertains to* are irreflexive relations. That is, no substitutions on the variable A in the formulas *A owns A* and *A appertains to A* yield significant statements. E.g., *Fido owns Fido, this dog owns this dog, this person appertains to this person* and *I am mine* are all meaningless.

I use *appertains to* rather than the more familiar *belongs to* because the latter is ambiguous between *appertains to* and *is a member of*. It is easy to see that these are different relations. If X appertains to A, then A must logically own X. But if A is a member of the Golf Club, it does not follow that the Golf Club owns A.

However, the thesis that *owns* and *appertains to* are irreflexive may be contested on various grounds. In the first place, an objector might observe that one can call A self-possessed. But this objection need not detain us long. *A is self-possessed* means *A is composed,* not *A possesses A*. It is a locution which belongs with other oddities such as *A is not himself, A is beside himself* and *A is a slave to his lower nature*. That the last one is not literally significant is clear from what has just been said. For as it is absurd to speak of A appertaining to A, so it is absurd to speak of A appertaining or being enslaved to a part of A, namely, his "lower nature".

Next, it may be objected that A can be said to own himself since he has powers of exclusive use, destruction and alienation over himself. As to the last two, he certainly has the powers to commit suicide and enslave himself, even though he may have no moral or legal right to do so. While as to the first, he surely has this power too; for he can be self-employed, and what is a self-employed man but one who uses himself? But this last contention will not do. *A is self-employed* does not mean that A uses himself; it means that he works for himself and not for another, or works on his own account, or is his own master. (To be one's own master is not, incidentally, the same as to be master of oneself. To be the former is to be self-employed, but to be the latter is to be self-controlled.) The reason why the intelligible *A is self-employed* cannot mean *A uses A* is that no statement of the latter form is intelligible, since *uses* is also an irreflexive relation. This is in turn the reason why *A owns A* is unintelligible, for (exclusive) *use* is the most important part of the meaning of *property*. On the other hand, the other components of the meaning of *property*, namely, destruction and alienation, are not irreflexive, since A can destroy himself and sell or give himself to B. He cannot, however, bequeath himself; he can only bequeath his body, say to a medical school; and his body is not identical with his person. To see this, it is only necessary to reflect that there are attributable to A a whole range of "personal predicates", such as *witty, irresolute* and *vain* which are not attributable to his body alone.[14] But although A cannot use himself or his person, he can use parts of himself. He can use his eyes or his shoulder, his feet or his wits.

Another possible objection against the irreflexivity of *owns* is that it is correct, and true, to say, e.g., that Magdalen College owns Magdalen College. But the answer is easy. This statement does not genuinely exemplify the formula *A owns A*, because in its first occurrence *Magdalen College* means *the Fellows of Magdalen College*, whereas in its second occurrence it means certain buildings, gardens, etc. However, the objection may be developed more plausibly as follows. Suppose that the Fellows of Magdalen are two, A and B, and that each has made himself the other's slave. Is it not now correct, and true, to say that the Fellows of Magdalen own the Fellows of Magdalen? The reply is that there seems to be a sense in which the statement is correct and true, but another sense in which it is meaningless. It seems to be true, in the collective sense of *all*, that all the Fellows own all the Fellows, since every Fellow owns and is owned by some Fellow. But it is not true, or false either, in the distributive sense of *all*, that each and all the Fellows own each and all the Fellows, since A cannot logically own A and B cannot logically own B. Accordingly, there seems to be one sense in which a class, but not an individual, can own itself.

[14] P. F. Strawson, *Individuals*, London, 1959, ch. 3, secs. 5, 6.

Even so, there only appears to be such a sense and there is none such really. This is because the concept of mutual enslavement is actually incoherent, for the following reasons. If A is to own B, then he must be able to use B. Moreover, if he is to be able to use B, he must be able to command B. This last point is true of all labour$_5$, hirelings as well as slaves; it cannot be used unless it is under its master's orders. Further, *commands* is an asymmetrical relation. If, in a certain relationship, A commands B, then B cannot also command A in that same relationship. The qualification "in a certain relationship" is necessary because it is perfectly possible for A to command B in one relationship and for B to command A in another relationship. In their employer/employee relationship, the squire commands his butler and not conversely. But this is quite compatible with the butler commanding the squire but not conversely in their captain/player relationship when both are members of the village cricket-team of which the butler is captain. Hence, the impossibility of mutual enslavement can be proved by the following dilemma:

Either A commands B or A does not command B, and not both
If A commands B then B does not command A
If B does not command A then B does not own A
If A does not command B then A does not own B
∴ Either B does not own A or A does not own B, and not both
∴ It is not the case both that A owns B and that B owns A.

This last objection to the irreflexivity of *owns* therefore also fails.

This dilemma also proves that *owns* is asymmetrical. This is because mutual enslavement is the only *prima facie* possible case of mutual ownership, since only men can be proprietors. 'Can Tom own Dick and conversely?' is at least *prima facie* an intelligible question. Whereas 'Can Tom own Sherwood Forest and conversely?', and *a fortiori*, 'Can Sherwood Forest own the New Forest and conversely?' are obviously absurd questions. In its standard or paradigm use, *owns* is also intransitive. If A owns B and B owns X, then A cannot own X. This is because, in this use, *owns* connotes *has the exclusive use of*, and it is impossible for both A and B to have the exclusive use of X. This objection does not apply, however, to forms of property which do not involve exclusive use, for instance, joint property. Thus, cases of the following sort could occur: A buys a wife who owns a house, whereupon the house becomes by law the joint property of A and of his wife. The following sort of case is also possible: A buys a wife who owns a house, whereupon the house becomes by law the property of A. One might, indeed, think that the possibility of this last type of case proves that *owns* is not intransitive. But this would be an error. For in such cases statements of the forms *A owns B, B owns X* and *A owns X* are not all true together, since at the moment when the third becomes true the second ceases to be so. Hence, in fine, in their standard or paradigm uses, the binary relation *owns* and its converse *appertains to* are irreflexive, asymmetrical and intransitive.

I am sure that the root cause of Locke's mistaken belief that statements of the form *A owns A* make sense is similar to that underlying his belief that it makes sense to speak of a man's owning his labour[1]. It is the existence in English of the pronouns *myself, yourself,* etc., combined with the assumption that the adjectives *my, your,* etc., in those pronouns resemble the *my* and *your* in *my book* and *your pen* in being possessive. But inspection of the actual uses of these pronouns will show that these are not to claim possession or to assert anything remotely connected with property, but to do something quite different. Their uses are in fact two. First, the reflexive use, which is to indicate that the object of a transitive verb is identical with its subject, or that the verb expresses a reflexive relation. E.g., *A wounded himself.* Secondly, the emphatic use, which is to indicate that the subject of the verb is indeed that subject and no other. E.g., *A himself has come,* where *himself* has the force of *in person.* The two uses may be combined in a single sentence, as in *A himself wounded himself.* In some other languages, the reflexive and emphatic uses are distinguished by the use of different words. Thus, the Latin, French and German translations of *A himself wounded himself* are respectively: *A ipse se vulneravit, A se blessa lui-même* and *A selbst verwundete sich.* Significantly, these Latin, French and German words, unlike their English equivalent, include no "possessive adjectives" as constituents; nowhere does there appear a *suus, son,* or *sein.* Consequently, they do not misleadingly suggest ownership in the way that the English words do. The reflexive and emphatic uses of these pronouns may both conveniently be called identificatory, since this is their essential function in both cases. The sense of *A himself wounded himself* is accurately rendered by *A and only A wounded A and only A.* The purpose of the reflexive use is to identify the object of the verb with its subject, A, thereby excluding all other possible objects, such as B. Similarly, the purpose of the emphatic use is to identify the subject of the verb with A, thereby excluding all other possible subjects, such as B.

5. CONCLUSION

Locke's justification of private property did not originate with him. The alleged right of self-ownership, which is the foundation of his theory, is asserted for instance in the Leveller R. Overton's tract of 1646, *An Arrow against all Tyrants:*

To every Individuall in nature is given an individual property by nature, not to be invaded or usurped by any: for every one as he is himselfe, so he hath a selfe propriety, else could he not be himselfe, and on this no second may presume to deprive any of, without manifest violation and affront to the very principles of nature, and of the Rules of equity and justice between man and man; mine and thine cannot be, except this be. . . .

As for the subsequent history of Locke's theory of property, it exerted a strong practical influence, but in opposite directions. In Locke's own hands, it was an important element in his justification of Private Capitalism. The crucial argument for this purpose is the one about "the turf my servant has cut", which I examined and rejected above (Sec. 3). A vital question in any discussion of property-rights is *how much* of a given sort of property a man may justifiably acquire. The effect of Locke's proposition (3) is to restrict the amount of property which a man may rightfully possess to that which he has himself produced or received in exchange for his products (Sec. 2). Initially, indeed, Locke imposes an additional restriction: A has a right to private property in only so much of his own works$_3$ as he can use and therefore will not be wasted. "As much as any one can make use of to any advantage of life before it spoils, so much he may by his labour fix a property in; whatever is beyond this is more than his share, and belongs to others." Later, however, Locke argues that this additional restriction may be transcended by means of money: all that A has to do is to exchange that part of his produce which is surplus to his needs for gold or silver, which do not spoil.[15] He argues further that the original restriction of A's property to that which he has himself produced may be transcended by the "turfs" argument. For the upshot of that argument is that, when A employs B, B's works$_3$ are rightly A's property. It is easy to see how the "gold" and the "turfs" arguments justify Private Capitalism. To become a capitalist, A must proceed as

---

[15] Locke, *l.c.*, ch. 5, secs. 31, 46–49.

follows. He must first produce more than he can consume, and exchange the surplus for money. With this money he must then on the one hand buy land, raw materials, tools, etc.; and on the other hand hire labour$_5$ to work them. Finally, he must sell the works$_3$ of this labour$_5$ for money, and thereby put himself in a position to repeat the same cycle of operations.

In the hands of others, however, Locke's doctrine was given a critical or Socialist turn. These took their stand on the original proposition (3) and, ignoring or rejecting the "turfs" argument, condemned as unjustified any property which a man possessed beyond what he had either produced himself or acquired in exchange therefor.[16]

It is curious to reflect that, if the uses of the adjective *my* in *my work$_1$* and in *myself* had not been mistaken for its possessive use; or if the English identificatory pronoun *myself*, like its equivalents in some other languages, did not include this "possessive adjective" as a constituent; then in all probability the world would have been without this ideology.[17]

APPENDIX: USES OF WORK AND OF LABOUR

Uses	Synonyms	Examples
$Work_1 = Labour_1$	$Working = Labouring$	*All work and no play makes Jack a dull boy.*
		The writing of Principia Mathematica *was a great labour.*
$Work_2 = Labour_2$	*Task*	*The work of converting the heathen is incomplete.*
		Hercules was set twelve labours.
$Work_3$	*Achievement*	Principia Mathematica *is a work by Whitehead and Russell.*
$Work_4$	*Product of force and distance*	*Jack did* 100 ft. lbs. of work.
$Labour_5$	*Labourers = Workers*	*Ford employs a lot of labour.*

---

[16] C. B. Macpherson, *The Political Theory of Possessive Individualism*, Oxford, 1962, ch. 3, sec. 4; ch. 5, sec. 2: A. J. Ryan, "Locke and the Dictatorship of the Bourgeoisie", *Political Studies*, June 1965, reprinted above, pp. 86–106.

[17] This paper was read to the central Ontario philosophical group on 13 November 1965.

POLITICAL OBLIGATION
AS MORALITY*

E. F. Carritt

✤

The essential difference between Locke and the political theorists we have been considering [i.e., Hobbes, Spinoza, Hume, and Rousseau] is that he believes in what he calls Laws of Nature or of Reason not dependent upon convention or upon states and governments. They are, in fact, mutual obligations really binding upon men, recognized by them as binding, and able to influence their behaviour. In the *Essay of Civil Government* Locke defines political power as 'a right of making laws with penalties . . . for the regulating and preserving of property, and of employing the force of the community, in the execution of such laws, and in defence of the commonwealth from foreign injury; and *all this only for the public good*'.[1] Men are naturally in 'a state of perfect freedom to order their actions and dispose of their possessions and persons, as they think fit, *within the bounds of the law of nature*'. This is a state of equality.[2] The law of nature

obliges every one; and *reason*, which is that law, teaches that . . . man has not liberty to destroy himself, or so much as any creature in his possession, but where some nobler use than its bare preservation calls for it. . . . All being equal, . . . no one ought to harm another in his life, health, liberty or possessions. . . . Every one, as he is bound to preserve himself, . . . so by the like reason, when his own preservation comes not in competition, ought he, as much as he can, to preserve the rest of mankind, and may not, unless it be to do justice to an offender, take away or impair the life, the liberty, health, limb, or goods of another.[3]

In transgressing the law of nature, the offender declares himself to live by another rule than that of reason and common equity, . . . and every

---

* Reprinted from E. F. Carritt, *Morals and Politics* (Oxford, 1935), pp. 72–79, by permission of the Clarendon Press, Oxford.
   [1] *Second Treatise* (1690), chap. I, § 3 (my italics). Cited throughout by chapter and section number. Cf. IX, § 131.
   [2] II, § 4.
   [3] II, § 6.

man, by the right he hath to preserve mankind in general, . . . hath a right
to punish the offender.[4]

Wherefore we punish aliens. Laws 'are only so far right, as they
are founded on the law of nature, by which they are to be regulated
and interpreted'.[5] Truth and keeping of faith belong to men as men,
and not as members of society.[6] This state of nature, contrary to
Hobbes, is the exact opposite of a state of war.[7]

Force without right, upon a man's person, makes a state of war, both
where there is, and is not a common judge, . . . because the aggressor
allows not time to appeal.[8] . . . Nay, where an appeal to the law, and
constituted judges, lies open, but the remedy is denied by a manifest pervert-
ing of justice, and a barefaced wresting of the laws to protect or indemnify
the violence or injuries of some man, or party of men; there it is hard
to imagine anything but a state of war: for wherever violence is used, and
injury done, though by hands appointed to administer justice, it is still
violence and injury, however coloured with the name, pretences, or forms
of law, the end whereof being to protect and redress the innocent, by an
unbiassed application of it to all who are under it; wherever that is not bona
fide done, war is made upon the sufferers, who having no appeal on earth
to right them, they are left to the only remedy in such cases, an appeal to
heaven.

Men's motive, then, in forming themselves into a society was to
avoid the possibility of a state of war; 'to protect and redress the
innocent'. For the great inconvenience of the state of nature was that
men were judges in their own case, as absolute monarchs are in society,[9] and that there was no impartial power to enforce promulgated
law.[10]

The natural liberty of man is to be free from any superior power; . . .
the liberty of man, in society, is to be under no other legislative power, but
that established by consent, in the commonwealth.[11]
Natural reason tells us that men, being once born, have a right to their
preservation, and consequently to meat and drink, and such other things
as nature affords for their subsistence.

[4] II, § 8.
[5] II, § 12.
[6] II, § 14. I do not think Locke is committed to denying that society favours
the development of our capacity to recognize obligations or laws of reason.
[7] III, § 19.
[8] III, §§ 19, 20.
[9] II, § 13.
[10] IX, §§ 124–6.
[11] IV, § 22.

The fruits of the earth and the beasts it feeds belong to mankind in common, but 'there must of necessity be a means to appropriate them some way or other, before they can be of any use, or at all beneficial to any particular man'.[12]

Though the earth, and all inferiour creatures be common to all men, yet every man has a property in his own person: this nobody has any right to but himself. The labour of his body, and the works of his hands, are properly his. Whatsoever then he removes out of the state that nature hath provided and left it in, he hath mixed his labour with, and joined to it something that is his own, and thereby makes it his property, . . . at least where there is enough, and as good, left in common for others.[13]

As much as any one can make use of to any advantage of life before it spoils, so much he may by labour fix a property in: whatever is beyond this, is more than his share and belongs to others.[14]

Every man has a right *before any other man* to inherit with his brethren his father's goods.[15]

Civil society, then, neither first creates nor at all diminishes man's natural liberty, that is, his rights to his body, subsistence, and labour. Laws are justifiable so far as they ensure every man the enjoyment of these rights by restraining every man from invading those of his neighbours. All that man resigns to the political community, when he enters it, is his other natural right of judging and punishing the infringement of these rights to the best of his power.[16] And therewith 'he has given a right to the commonwealth to employ his force, for the execution of the judgements of the commonwealth'.[17]

From all this it follows that the rule of an absolute monarch or of any arbitrary power from which there is no appeal to the impartial administration of promulgated law, is no civil government. To suppose the rulers freed from the restraint of law

is to think, that men are so foolish that they take care to avoid what mischiefs may be done them by pole-cats, or foxes; but are content, nay think it safety, to be devoured by lions. But whatever flatterers may talk to amuse people's understandings, it hinders not men from feeling: and when they perceive, that any man, in what station soever, is out of the bounds of the civil society which they are of, and that they have no appeal on earth

---

[12] v, §§ 25–6.
[13] v, § 27.
[14] v, § 31.
[15] xvi, § 190 (*my italics*). Cf. *First Treatise*, ix, § 88.
[16] vii, § 87.
[17] vii, § 88.

against any harm they may receive from him, they are apt to think themselves in the state of nature, in respect of him whom they find to be so: and
to take care, as soon as they can, to have that safety and security in civil
society, for which it was instituted, and for which only they entered
into it. [18]

It is, then, only to the whole community or *in practice to the
majority*,[19] that men have resigned this right of judgement and executive. What they had not they could not resign, and they had no arbitrary right to act against the laws of nature and reason.[20] The
legislature consequently has not arbitrary power, rather it acts *pur-
suant to a trust*,[21] which is violated by all that does the people harm.[22]
If it be asked who is to judge whether this fiduciary power is justly
employed, we may ask in reply: 'Who shall be judge whether his
trustee or deputy acts well and according to the trust reposed in him,
but he who deputes him, and must by having deputed him, have still a
power to discard him when he fails in his trust?'[23] The government
may then be dissolved for breach of trust, but the dissolution of
government must be distinguished from the dissolution of the society,[24] and even the dissolution of a society does not reduce its
members to a state of war, but only to the state of nature in which
they are still obliged by the laws of reason.

Such in the main is Locke's account of political obligation, by no
means without ambiguities or confusions and even manifest errors of
historic fact and of detail, yet fundamentally, I think, sound, as opposed to all those we have been considering. No doubt it is cramped by
the necessity for justifying a glorious revolution of Whig landowners,
as Hobbes was by his need to legitimize whatever king might reign.
But even its reverence for property is reasoned and, in its time, when
labour was not highly socialized, very reasonable. The possibility of a
consistent account of allegiance is secured by founding it on our
obligations to our neighbour instead of them on it and it on self-
interest. Against that merit its failings weigh light.

These weaknesses are mainly connected with the contract, which

18 vii, §§ 93–4.
19 viii, § 96.
20 xi, § 135.
21 xi, § 134 (*my italics*); cf. xiii, § 149, 'a fiduciary power to act for certain
ends.'
22 xiv, § 166.
23 xix, § 240.
24 xix, § 211.

is almost as superfluous to Locke as it was to Hobbes. For Hobbes, as we have seen, it was merely a smoke-screen, which succeeded in blinding Rousseau to the difference between the wills of the majority and my own will. For Locke it is an assumption which, if or when it was true, would reinforce an obligation, already recognized, to support any *de facto* government so long as it effects justice and well-being, but no longer. And it will probably not be questioned that the king who has taken an oath to the constitution and the soldier or civil servant who is in its pay are under stricter responsibilities of loyalty than ordinary citizens.[25] In attempting to show that a contract perhaps made by our remote forefathers is certainly binding upon us, Locke is driven to the usual arguments. He allows that men are not in fact bound by their fathers' compacts, but by accepting their fathers' land, if there be any, when they come of age, they put themselves under the government of the community.[26] This would make landless men outlaws; so Locke continues that tacit contract is involved in accepting lodging for a week or in travelling on the highway.[27] But those who have only thus tacitly contracted are at liberty to quit their possessions or the highway and therewith their allegiance. This is not convincing.

A second weakness is in the argument that majority rule is somehow specially consonant with the law of reason, and not merely a practical expedient. Certainly Locke did not escape the utilitarianism of his age, which, for all his superior conception of justice as a law of reason, inclined him to assume that the satisfaction of the greater number would always be just.

But, in spite of these inconclusions, Locke undoubtedly distinguishes men's duties from their interests, and justice from the production of the most happiness. He is one of those who think we ought to obey a government so long as it on the whole secures justice and happiness. We have somehow contracted to obey it on those terms, but we ought to obey it even if we had not. With all Locke's faults, making some allowance for his time, his account of political obligations seems to me the best.[28]

---

[25] Cf. Hume, *Treatise*, III. ii. 8.

[26] *Civil Government*, VIII, § 117.

[27] §§ 119–21. We ought then to be under equal obligation to the government of every land where we travel, but cf. XIX, 243.

[28] It is true that Locke was tarred with the same brush of psychological hedonism as Rousseau (cf. *Essay on the Human Understanding*, I. iii, § 12), but in his political theory he forgets this and is unaffected by it, whereas Rousseau's is distorted by it. Cf. II. xxviii, § 5, 'Good and evil are nothing but pleasure or pain.'

CONSENT IN THE POLITICAL THEORY OF JOHN LOCKE*

John Dunn

It is widely agreed that the notion of consent plays a central role in the political theory which Locke sets out in the *Two Treatises of Government*. Mr Plamenatz, Mr Gough, Professor Kendall and Professor Waldmann all discuss the notion as though it were the fulcrum of that theory. It is also widely assumed that the *Two Treatises of Government* is a simple abstract of Locke's formal political reflexion and that it must contain in a readily ascertainable form all the basic premises of his political reasoning. More pointedly (since that is the character which works of political theory are supposed properly to display) it is presumed that it contains both a theory of political obligation and a theory of how political life both is and should be conducted, a normative and descriptive theory of the polity. These assumptions do not appear at first sight very misleading—it might seem that, if true, they would designate clearly the area to be analysed and, if false, they can readily be seen to be so. But paradigms for the conduct of investigations can do much to determine the perceived results of the investigations.[1] The point of this paper is to discuss a typical misunderstanding which seems to me to derive from an improper paradigm.

The place of consent within the theory of the *Two Treatises* is simple, if frequently misunderstood. But government by consent is too much of a contemporary shibboleth and Locke a historical figure of too much eminence for the theory to have been left intact in its seventeenth-century context. 'Consent', so the reasoning seems to go, is a necessary condition for political legitimacy in the *Two Treatises*.

---

* Reprinted from *The Historical Journal*, Vol. 10 (1967), 153–182, by permission of the editor and author. Some footnotes have been condensed or eliminated.

[1] I am using this notion very vulgarly. For two perceptive examples of the use to which it can be put in historical investigation see E. H. Gombrich, *Art and Illusion* (London, 1960), and T. S. Kuhn, *The Structure of Scientific Revolutions* (Chicago, 1962).

Government by consent is the proper mode of government.[2] Locke was a great liberal philosopher. Hence the *Two Treatises of Government* must needs advocate government by consent, that is, must contain a theory of consent as the proper guarantee for governmental legitimacy. 'The argument of the *Treatise* is the government is not legitimate unless it is carried on with the consent of the governed. But the *Treatise* says little indeed about how government should be organized in order to have the consent of the governed.'[3] Government by consent means that the proper conduct of government is predicated on the psychological state of the governed. Hence Locke's account of consent is to be criticized for setting up inadequate criteria for judging the continuing psychological relationship between governors and governed. But this is not what Locke's theory of consent is about. It is a theory of how individuals become subject to political obligations and how legitimate political societies can arise. It is not in any sense whatsoever a theory of how government should be organized.

This paper is intended to give an account of the place of consent in the *Two Treatises*. To do this convincingly, I attempt to do three things. Firstly I claim that what would have been, if he had formally elaborated them, Locke's theory of political obligation and his theory of the state are not set out in the *Two Treatises*, and that his theory of political obligation, in so far as it can be discerned in his other writings,

---

[2] Or, alternatively, some form of it is importantly not the proper mode of government—cf. Leo Strauss, *Natural Right and History* (Chicago, 1953), pp. 202–51 and C. B. Macpherson, *The Political Theory of Possessive Individualism* (Oxford, 1962). Perhaps also the brilliant, if wayward, work of Willmoore Kendall, *John Locke and the Doctrine of Majority-Rule* (Urbana, Illinois 1941. Reprinted 1959).

[3] John Plamenatz, *Man and Society* (London, 1963), 1,209. See also pp. 211, 227; but cf. p. 210, 'Locke's *Treatise* is not concerned to justify any form of government; it is concerned rather to assert the right of the people to resist their rulers when they are misruled by them.' The implications of this are hardly grasped in the rest of the account given. Plamenatz's treatment in *Man and Society*, 1, 209–41, and its development of his criticisms in his *Consent, Freedom, and Political Obligation* (Oxford, 1938), esp. pp. 7–8 is (with the exception of some parts of Kendall's book cited in footnote 2 above) the most careful and penetrating analysis of Locke's position on consent yet produced (but see also footnote 99 below). Were it not for the misunderstanding of what Locke's theory of consent was about, it would be most impressive. For other accounts, which share the misunderstanding, see T. Waldmann, 'A Note on John Locke's Theory of Consent', *Ethics*, LXVIII (i); J. W. Gough, *John Locke's Political Philosophy* (Oxford, 1956), ch. III, pp. 46–71; C. B. Macpherson, op. cit. pp. 194–262 and for a more incidental example C. W. Cassinelli, *The Politics of Freedom* (Seattle, 1961), pp 86–101, 177. An extremely helpful brief treatment is Raymond Polin, *La Politique Morale de John Locke* (Paris, 1960), pp. 209–12.

differs sharply from that assumed by most criticisms of the *Two Treatises;* that what this book does in fact contain is an exposition of certain necessary limitations upon political obligation; and that we make both a historical and a philosophical mistake when we suppose that theory is incompatible with the general theory indicated elsewhere in his writings. Secondly, I set out a brief outline of the argument of the *Two Treatises.* Thirdly, I examine the precise implications of the notion of consent used in this work.

Any general theory of political obligation must derive it, at least in part, from descriptive features of the human social situation. Even a purely theological theory must include statements which designate in the descriptive language of the society concerned the person or persons to whom obedience is owned. But the general account of the basis of political duty to which Locke appears to have held throughout his life as a writer has much more than such a minimal reference to the society for which it was devised. It was indeed, as any such general theory must be, a compound of sociological banality and ethical truism. But more importantly, since his ethical theory was at all times set out in theological terms, political duty was always discussed as a duty to God. From the *Treatises on the Civil Magistrate*,[4] the *Essays on the Law of Nature*[5] to the *Two Treatises* itself,[6] to incidental observations on the basis of property rights in his notebooks[7] and even to the *Reasonableness of Christianity*,[8] all political obligations are set in

---

[4] John Locke, *Two Tracts on Government*, ed. P. Abrams (Cambridge, 1967), pp. 172, 201 (231–2). (Cited hereafter as Abrams (ed.) op. cit.)

[5] John Locke, *Essays on the Law of Nature*, ed. W. Von Leyden (Oxford, 1954), esp. pp. 181–9. (Hereafter cited as Von Leyden (ed.) op. cit.)

[6] John Locke, *Two Treatises of Government*, ed. Peter Laslett (Cambridge, 1964). See esp. 2nd Treatise, para. 77, ll. 1–5 (pp. 336–7): 'God having made Man such a Creature, that, in his own Judgment, it was not good for him to be alone, put him under strong Obligations of Necessity, Convenience, and Inclination to drive him into *Society*, as well as fitted him with Understanding and Language to continue and enjoy it.' The Abrams, Von Leyden, and Laslett editions cited in footnotes 4–6 above are all outstanding pieces of editorial work and their introductions contain major contributions to the analysis of Locke's thought. I should like to acknowledge a heavy debt to all three, most particularly to Mr Laslett. This work is cited hereafter as Laslett (ed.), op. cit.

[7] Bodleian Library, MSS. Locke, c.28, fo. 113 v (Homo ante et post lapsum), and fo. 139, 'Morality'. The Bodleian collection of Locke manuscripts are hereafter cited simply as 'MSS. Locke'.

[8] John Locke, *The Reasonableness of Christianity*. Cited from *The Worke of John Locke* (7th ed.) (London, 1768), III, 1–99. (Cited hereafter as *Reasonableness. Works.* vol. etc.) In this work Locke does not discuss political duties specifically; but the argument that the acceptance of the Christian revelation renders

a single dominating context. They are as they are because of the nature of fallen man, capable of reason but liable to sin, because of the character of the natural world, and because both of these are the work of God. Perhaps the simplest and clearest expression of this construction of political duty out of human rationality and the human biological situation comes in a note written in his journal for 15 July 1679 on the law of nature.[9] 'If he finds that god has made him & all other men in a state wherein they cannot subsist without society & has given them judgment to discern what is capable of preserving & maintaining that society can he but conclude that he is obliged & that god requires him to follow those rules which conduce to the preserving of society.' Political obligation is a conclusion of reason based on the necessary features of specifically human biological existence, an elementary theorem of the human condition.

It is a mistake to suppose that if Locke had at any point in his literary life been asked the simple moral question, 'Why should men obey legitimate authority in a legitimate political society?', he would have replied that they had consented to do so. Consent may explain the origins of political legitimacy. It may indicate how it is that a particular individual at some specific time becomes liable to particular political obligations. But it is simply not the reason why Locke thought most men obliged to obey the legitimate exercise of political authority. The notion of consent is deployed in the *Two Treatises* in order to expound certain limits on the possible extent of political obligation. Plainly it could not have achieved this exposition plausibly if it were incompatible with his general notions of political obligation. But the general ground of political obligation is not what Locke was attempting to discuss in the *Two Treatises* and to suppose that he would have written the same book if it had been what he was attempting to discuss is jejune. More precisely, consent denotes the occasion of incurring political obligations. To suppose that it must therefore constitute the ground of these obligations is to make the error of confusing the occasion of incurring an obligation with the general ground of the duty of honouring it. It is not that the obligation incurred on the specific occasion is different in *kind* from the general obligation; rather that the nature of the occasion is defined by the context of potential

---

conveniently otiose the full deduction of the law of nature has the effect of reducing complex ethical calculations to the moral truisms of an existing Christian social morality. (There is no full modern edition of *The Reasonableness*).

[9] MSS. Locke f. 3, fos. 201–2.

obligations. In other words, if we are to understand what Locke meant by consent it is vain to attempt to extrapolate it solely from the *subjective* characteristics of the occasion on which consent is given. Consent cannot simply be understood as a subjective fact, a fact about the psychology of the individual. It has to be understood primarily as a legal fact about the divine order of nature.

The argument of the *Two Treatises* is very simple in outline. '. . . Men being all the Workmanship of one Omnipotent, and infinitely wise Maker; All the Servants of one Sovereign Master, sent into the World by his order and about his business, they are his Property, whose Workmanship they are, made to last during his, not one anothers Pleasure.'[10] They belong to God and hence they have no right to destroy themselves.[11] All their duties and responsibilities are owed in the first place to God and the *duty* of self-preservation is perhaps the most fundamental of these. It is natural to describe it as a right held against other human beings but it must be understood primarily as a duty towards God. A man can only transfer to others a right which he himself possesses.[12] The possession of rights is a jural not an empirical matter. It can most easily be elucidated by examining the ethical rules which hold between men who confront each other outside any framework of positive law.[13] The degree of biological differentiation is not so great as to justify the inference that any human being has been created for the benefit of another,[14] and the identity of status implied by their common relationship with God precludes the possibility of such a doctrine. Hence it is only as a result of their own voluntary

[10] Laslett (ed.), op. cit. 2nd Treatise, para. 6, ll. 10–14 (p. 289).

[11] *Ibid.* 19–22 (p. 289): 'Every one as he is *bound to preserve himself*, and not quit his station wilfully; so by the like reason when his own Preservation comes not in competition, ought he, as much as he can, *to preserve the rest of Mankind* . . . '

[12] Laslett (ed.), op. cit. 2nd Treatise, para. 23, ll. 4–9 (p. 302).

[13] This relationship, the state of nature, is a convenient abstraction which has numerous empirical instances; but it is not specified at all in terms of empirical criteria of social simplicity or complexity. That it *can* have instances is dialectically important to Locke since it excludes most of Filmer's arguments; but the argument itself would remain intact if there had never been a single instance of an unequivocal state of nature in human history. It is an error to suppose that it has somehow been vitiated by the researches of Sir Henry Maine and his successors. It is a theological not a sociological argument. That it was ideologically important, given the legalistic and obsessively historical conventions of English political dispute at the time and given the level of intellectual competence likely to be displayed by admirers of Sir Robert Filmer, is obvious enough but in no way affects the status of the argument itself.

[14] Laslett (ed.), op cit. 2nd Treatise, para. 6, ll. 15–19 (p. 289).

actions that men can confer legitimate authority upon other men (though not all political duties are instances of the rights of authorities to demand obedience; where a political authority has broken its trust and an individual is threatened, he may be obliged not to resist the authority, even though the latter has no *rights* over him, if the effect upon his fellow men makes such resistance intolerably costly).[15] Voluntary action does not, of course, imply the absence of motive, even of overwhelmingly powerful motive. Nor does it imply a formal verbal commitment. All that it implies is the absence of coercion. Consent in this fairly clear, though not behaviourally very precise, sense is a necessary condition for the legitimate authority of one man over another. But it is not a sufficient condition. Men's psychological reach exceeds their juristic grasp. As biological organisms, their capacity to assent is not confined to those cases in which the law of nature legally empowers them to do so. Legitimate authority is not co-extensive either with the totality of legally permissible moral commitments nor with the totality of actual psychological assents. Certain sorts of injustice must always destroy the legitimacy of political authority, even if those who suffer them are physically coerced or ideologically befuddled into submitting to them. Locke's theory does not make consent equivalent to either efficient physical control or successful conditioning. Its most essential element remains a sort of formal rationality which no contingent truths of psychology could impugn.

The sole source of legitimate authority (though, as said above, not the sole basis of political duty) is, then, the rational consent of individuals. What they can rationally consent to is limited by their own rights. One major limitation on their own rights to dispose of themselves, the suicide taboo, is the basis of the account of necessary

---

[15] Laslett (ed.), op. cit. 2nd Treatise, para. 176, ll. 34–40 (p. 404): 'He that troubles his Neighbour without a Cause, is punished for it by the Justice of the Court he appeals to. And he that *appeals to Heaven*, must be sure that he has Right on his side; and a Right too that is worth the Trouble and Cost of the Appeal, as he will answer at a Tribunal, that cannot be deceived, and will be sure to retribute to every one according to the Mischiefs he hath created to his Fellow-Subjects; that is, any part of Mankind.' But cf. para. 208 (p. 422) and para. 225 (p. 433) where it is merely stated that private individuals will not in fact exercise such a right when their grievance is not widely shared; not that it would be wrong of them to do so. What is in question here is simply the point that a right is defeasible by other conflicting rights; cf. Laslett (ed.), op. cit. 1st Treatise, para. 42 (p. 188) for the possible conflict between rights based on 'Justice' and those based on 'Charity'. See also my article, 'Justice and the Interpretation of Locke's Political Theory,' *Political Studies*, 1968.

limitations on political authority given in the *Two Treatises*.[16] Because men cannot kill themselves, they cannot give to others a right to kill them—though they can make it possible for others to punish them, if they break the law of nature, since this involves no transfer of rights[17] and is a merely prudential calculation. Hence any act of a legitimate or illegitimate political authority which unjustly threatens the life of an individual subject voids the political rights of the authority.[18] In this way the *Two Treatises* extrapolates the right of resistance to unjust power from the suicide taboo. This structure of argument is the context in which Locke's discussion of consent in the *Two Treatises* is set.

Besides employing the term 'consent' elaborately in the *Two Treatises*, there are numerous other pieces of writing, published and unpublished, in which Locke makes use of it in an analytically important way. It would be possible to examine the various contexts in chronological order; indeed to do so would have substantial analytical advantages. But any such advantages would be drastically offset by the inordinate repetition and huge length that such a method of presentation would demand. Hence, at this point, the works are merely listed and subsequently they are referred to only in order to cast light on the role which the notion has in the *Two Treatises* itself. It will be convenient to begin with an interpretation of Mr Plamenatz's; that Locke took consent to mean 'a voluntary act intended by the doer of it to give other people a right they would otherwise not have'.[19] This strong sense of the notion may well be necessary for the execution of the enterprise which Mr Plamenatz attributes to Locke in writing the *Two Treatises*. But is it what Locke himself meant? He seems, rather, and in his other writings as much as in the *Two Treatises* to use the

---

[16] Laslett (ed.), op. cit. 2nd Treatise, paras. 6, 23, 56, 135, 137, 149, 168, 172. Also 197–243, etc.

[17] When men break the law of nature, their jural status collapses and they become liable to the executive power of the law of nature in the hands of those upon whom they have legally made war. The basis upon which sovereign authorities exercise political power is this executive power of the law of nature ceded to them by their subjects. (See Laslett (ed.), op. cit. 2nd Treatise, paras. 7–11 etc.)

[18] It doesn't, of course as emphasized in footnote 15 above, void all the social duties of the subject—his right of resistance in the circumstance is contingent on a reasonably low cost to others of its exercise. But in so far as his duty to obey the sovereign could previously be expressed as a right of the sovereign to exact obedience, it can no longer be so expressed. Men's duties to God—and hence to their fellow-men—are more demanding than their duties towards those set in authority over them.

[19] Plamenatz, *Man and Society*, I, 227.

term consent, like assent, for the uncoerced acceptance of whatever disposition, of a practice, sentiment, or opinion. Clearly in behaving in such a manner men need not at all be *intending* to proclaim their recognition of a set of duties, still less to create a set of duties for themselves *ex nihilo*. What is suggested is clearly not that in doing X, men are intending to do *Y;* but rather that doing X may be construed as doing Y. What enables one to construe an example of one category of actions as an example of another category of actions in such a case must necessarily be a feature of the context in which the action is performed, not some peculiarly subtle feature of the state of mind of the agent at the time of decision. Plamenatz criticizes Locke for making duties which are essentially contextual contingent purely on the psychological states of individuals, and then in prudent concern at the anarchic implications of so doing, promptly rendering this psychological criterion nugatory.[20] I shall attempt to argue, in contrast, that there are no duties in Locke's philosophy (except the duty to worship God) which are not largely contextual in their specification; that consent is crudely behavioural in its form and that no very complex features of the mind of the agent are relevant to its identification. There are complicated philosophical problems which arise over questions of the sense in which one may be said to intend the consequences of one's actions[21] and it might be supposed that these arise even more critically over the issue of how one could construe consenting to some state of affairs as consenting to some other state of affairs. But Locke deliberately uses the notion in such an unspecific manner and for such a limited purpose that this line of approach seems wholly to miss the point.

In the *Two Treatises* men are said to consent to many different states of affairs and to do so in many different ways. Consent is said to be present at the inception of legitimate polities. It occurs on every occasion at which an individual by explicit or implicit choice becomes a member of a legitimate political community. It appears whenever a community chooses its representatives in the manner to which it has previously consented and whenever these representatives vote. It is responsible for the rise of a money economy and it is an attribute of

---

[20] Plamenatz, *Man and Society*, i, 209–52; esp. pp. 277–8 (see also Plamenatz, *Consent, Freedom, and Political Obligation* pp. 6–8). These criticisms seem precisely to be met by a consideration of those broader features of Locke's argument here emphasized.

[21] See, for example, G. E. M. Anscombe, *Intention* (Ithaca, N.Y. 1963), esp. pp. 37–49.

every subsequent monetary transaction. It is also displayed by those who deliberately (though not necessarily enthusiastically) participate in the unjust practices of their rulers. Rather fewer circumstances present any reliable indication of the absence of consent. Simple coercion is perhaps the clearest. Submission is just *not* the same as consent. Absolute monarchies also to some extent lack its sanction or at least, more unequivocally, such of them as are of any scale or degree of social sophistication and complexity. Most revealingly of all, those who do not specifically participate in the immoral actions of their rulers cannot be said to have consented to the actions. Clearly here an axiom of interpretation is being invoked, rather than a bet about the states of mind of the population. The criteria needed before one can be presumed to have done wrong are much more searching than those needed to establish that one has done right.

The *Two Treatises of Government* was written not as a set of instructions in how to institute legitimate political societies *ab initio*, but as an abridgement of a particular tradition of constitutionalist thought. It was intended to draw out the implications of one conception of an existing political community. It aimed to restore a previous political health; not to initiate but to revert.[22] Hence it is easier to understand the force and bearing of its conceptions in the context of concrete behavior which they are designed to explicate. Consent inside settled political societies appears overtly at three points, at the occasion on which an individual becomes a member of the political community and at the points at which the community chooses its representatives or these chosen representatives make laws. There are two sorts of membership in a political community, temporary and permanent, and

---

[22] For the important historical basis of these observations see Laslett (ed.), op. cit. Introduction, esp. pp. 44–91. Most clearly and crudely, this point is put in the very important letter which Locke wrote to his friend Edward Clarke on 8 February 1689 on the meetings of the Convention Parliament, the most illuminating document that we have available for gauging Locke's attitude to the particular form of the Revolution Settlement. (The importance of this document seems to have escaped previous interpreters of Locke's politics.) '. . . the settlement of the nation upon the sure grounds of peace and security is put into their hands, which can no way so well be done as by restoring our ancient government; the best possible that ever was, if taken and put together all of a piece in its original constitution. If this has not been invaded men have done ill to complain, and if it has men must certainly be so wise by feeling as to know where the frame has been put out of order, or if amiss; and for that now they have an opportunity offered to find remedies, and set up a constitution, that may be lasting, for the security of civil rights and the liberty and property of all the subjects of the nation.' *Locke and Clarke* (ed. Benjamin Rand) (Oxford, 1927), p. 289.

two corresponding ways of incurring it, tacit and explicit (or express) consent. Some form of consent is necessary because of the 'State all Men are naturally in . . . that is, a *State of perfect Freedom* to order their Actions, and dispose of their Possessions, and Persons as they think fit, within the bounds of the Law of Nature, without asking leave, or depending upon the Will of any other Man.'[23] Men can only consent for themselves; they cannot, for instance, do so for their children,[24] any more than they can sin for their children.[25] But to stress, in this way, the irreducible necessity of individual consent for the legitimacy of political authority raises obvious problems.[26] For when does any such consent take place? And how is it given? It is, Locke thought, the type of occasion on which it *is* normally given which leads people to ask such questions or, more simply, to assume erroneously that they are naturally subjects.[27] This is hardly surprising since it is not a necessary condition for the giving of consent that there should be *any* 'Expressions of it at all'.[28] If a government is legitimate almost any adult behaviour within the boundaries of the country—that is, all behaviour except emigration—constitutes consent. Why should this be so? There are two possible reasons. It might be the case that all persons who live in a certain geographical area do in fact share a certain attitude of mind towards the political authorities of such an area. But Locke plainly does not believe anything so odd. The only other possibility is that such a situation in itself implies certain *prima facie* duties; that the

---

[23] Laslett (ed.), op. cit. 2nd Treatise, para. 4, ll. 2–6 (p. 287). See also para. 114, ll. 5–11 (pp. 362–3) and para. 119, ll. 1–3 (p. 365) etc.

[24] Laslett (ed.), op. cit. 2nd Treatise para. 116, ll. 14–19 (p. 364), para. 118, ll. 11–21 (p. 365); para. 193, ll. 1–8 (p. 413), etc.

[25] *Reasonableness. Works*, iii, 3, 5, etc, for the interpretation of Adam's original sin and the insistence that it could not simply be said to *cause* the sins of his descendants (a necessary condition, here, distinguished from a sufficient condition); esp. p. 5, 'every one's sin is charged upon himself only'.

[26] It is perhaps necessary to emphasize that the problems had been raised already interminably by Robert Filmer. (See *Patriarcha and other Political Works of Sir Robert Filmer*, ed. P. Laslett, Oxford, 1949, pp. 81, 82, 189, 217, 218, 224–6, 243, 244, 273, 274. etc.)

[27] Laslett (ed.), op. cit. 2nd Treatise, para. 117, ll. 8–13 '. . . thus *the Consent of Free-men, born under Government*, which only *makes them Members of it*, being given separately in their turns, as each comes to be of Age, and not in a multitude together; People take no notice of it, and thinking it not done at all, or not necessary, conclude they are naturally Subjects as they are Men', and see para. 114, ll. 5–11 (pp. 362–3). Locke himself seems sometimes to condone such an empirically plausible error; cf. his taking 'countrymen', 'those who were born in the same country or tract of ground' as an example of a 'natural relation'. *Hum. Und.* 1, 294, (Bk. 2 C. 28 S. 2).

[28] Laslett (ed.) op. cit. 2nd Treatise, para. 120, l. 13 (p. 366).

duties are derived from the context and can, at most, be voided by considerations about the state of mind of the subject.

The circumstances in which a man cannot be said to have consented are confined to those in which he has been coerced. Anyone who voluntarily derives benefits from an existing political society incurs political obligations towards it.[29] This is because the setting up of a political society is the creation of a jural space, as well as of a physical protection; both of which are designed to secure the enjoyment of the participating individuals and both of which, at the level of social development reached in seventeenth-century England, as in many places, are necessary conditions for the existence of any such security. In such societies the lives, liberties and properties of the citizens are guaranteed by the legal system as rights and protected by the political system as goods. It is as recognized rights, that is to say, in Locke's terminology, as 'regulated by the laws', that they are in fact protected; and this legal protection of real goods in such societies is empirically necessary for their real protection. The mixture of empirical and ethical considerations is subtle and its exposition is more than a little muddled by Locke's need, in setting out his notion of the 'state of nature', to defend it against the vulgar and polemically effective Filmerian critique of man's natural freedom.[30] To make the situation somewhat clearer it is convenient to consider two recent critical analyses of the relation of succession to property to this account; those of Mr Plamenatz and Professor Macpherson.[31] Mr Plamenatz is struck by the contradiction between Locke's claim that inheritance of prop-

---

[29] Laslett (ed.), op. cit. 2nd Treatise, para. 119, ll. 9–22 (pp. 365–6). 'The difficulty is, what ought to be look'd upon as a *tacit Consent,* and how far it binds, i.e. how far any one shall be looked on to have consented, and thereby to have submitted to any Government where, he has made no Expressions of it at all. And to this I say, that every Man, that hath any Possession, or Enjoyment, of any part of the Dominions of any Government, doth thereby give his *tacit Consent,* and is as far forth obliged to Obedience to the Laws of that Government, during such Enjoyment, as any one under it; whether this his Possession be of Land, to him and his Heirs for ever, or a Lodging only for a Week; or whether it be barely travelling freely on the Highway; and in Effect, it reaches as far as the very being of any one within the Territories of that Government.' *N.B.* What is in question is 'how far any one shall be looked to on have consented . . . where he has made no Expressions of it at all' (ll. 11–13).

[30] For the elements of this account see Laslett (ed.), op. cit. 2nd Treatise, paras. 95–101 (pp. 348–52); para. 108, ll. 1–10 (pp. 357–8); para. 111, ll. 1–17, esp. ll. 4–5 (pp. 360–1); and esp. paras. 123–7 (pp. 368–70); also, paras. 128–31 (pp. 370–1).

[31] Plamenatz, *Man and Society,* 1, 226–7. C. B. Macpherson, *The Political Theory of Possessive Individualism* (Oxford, 1962), pp. 247–51 (and cf. Alan Ryan, 'Locke and the Dictatorship of the Bourgeoisie', *Political Studies,* XIII, no. 2 (June 1965), 219–30; esp. 226–7).

erty implies consent to the political authority of the society in which the property is situated and his inclusion of the natural right of bequest within the natural right of property. This hiatus is certainly the fault of Locke; but it is a flaw in his presentation of his argument, the inadvertency of his phrasing, rather than a flaw in the argument itself. The misunderstanding arises in two areas: in the failure to take account of the fact that Locke's natural rights are not unitary in their specification, and in the misapprehension of just how Locke defines the political relationship.

The situation is as follows: (1) A man institutes a government to protect his property. (2) The government passes laws which regulate the status of the property at all subsequent stages. (3) What the property *now* is is what the legal rules specify.[32] (For Locke, as for any other observer, seventeenth-century English property rights were a highly complex and artificial phenomenon, specified by the law. This did not mean that they were unnatural, in the sense of morally improper—though Locke himself certainly thought that some exercises of property rights which were legally impeccable were morally wrong —but they certainly were not natural in his eyes in any restricted, biologically-given, sense. That is just not the sort of notion which his notorious 'natural right to property' advances.) (4) Hence no man can possess the property without becoming liable to (*sc,* in Locke's terminology, 'consenting to') the rules. (5) Hence, to accept property implies accepting the rules which regulate it as legally valid, accepting the legitimacy of the legal sovereign, implies in fact political obligation. Plamenatz fails to take account of just what is implied in joining a political society. A member of a political society accepts *all* rules made by the society.[33] What a man's property is in the state of nature is what he has legitimately accumulated. What his property is in the polity is what the laws say it is. (This does not mean that *any* law which specifies what his property is (e.g. a law for the expropriation of Jews) is necessarily binding. But it does mean that nothing which is

---

[32] See especially Laslett (ed.), op. cit. 2nd Treatise, para. 120, ll. 1–21 (p. 366).

[33] This is an exaggeration. There are various exceptions. Rules which command actions to which the individual does not have the legal authority to consent (under the law of nature); rules which are not properly arrived at under the constitution of the country; rules which order the performance of actions which are intrinsically. wicked do not oblige subjects. All statements made in this section of the text are only true *ceteris paribus.* The exceptions listed in this note must always be kept in mind. Political obligations in Locke never involve *per se* consent to actions which are in principle wrong.

not so specified according to the legal rules *is* his property unless the specifying rule as such is illegitimate.) Property right is a legal right in form like any other right. This does not sound much like the Locke whom we all know. Indeed if it were all that Locke said about property, then clearly the Locke whom we all know would be a figment of the historical imagination (an exaggeration). But, of course, it is not. No express limits are implied logically in the conception of laws which the sovereign may pass to regulate property. But all such laws are subject to invalidation by the higher principle of the law of nature. A law which had the effect of removing a man's property without his consent would be in breach of the law of nature. But such a law could in general only be produced without a man's consent, if it did not meet the criteria for positive legality in the society. For what a man consents to in joining a society is precisely the positive law-making system.[34]

However, there are more exacting practical implications to the law of nature than this suggests.[35] There may be no internal legal grounds which make invalid the (formally legal) arbitrary and malicious confiscation of property; but higher law considerations provide no support for such unjust enactments and it is not clear that the victims would be in any but the (positive) legal sense obliged to comply. To suppose that there are (positive) legal reasons why a formally valid law can be voided for moral impropriety is a logical error. To suppose that all formally valid laws are morally obligatory is a moral error. Neither error is made by Locke. Legally correct rules which arbitrarily deprive anyone of his property are at best dubiously binding. Every man has a *prima facie* right to inherit property bequeathed to him and an arbitrary legal interference with such a right would not be morally binding on the injured party. But such *prima facie* rights in no way exempt an inheritor from holding the property on precisely the terms on which its previous owner held it. The property which the inheritor has a natural right to inherit *is* what the rules specify, a set of rights with contingent duties. The rights can to some

---

[34] More precisely, what man consents to is a continuing decision-procedure. This is what *constitutes* a political society (see Laslett (ed.), op. cit. 2nd Treatise, para. 95, ll. 4–14 (pp. 348–9); para. 96, ll. 1–17 (pp. 349–50); para. 97, ll. 1–14 (p. 350); para. 98, ll. 1–18 (pp. 350–1); para. 99, ll. 1–11 (p. 351); para. 134, ll. 11–21 (p. 374); para. 141, ll. 1–16 (pp. 380–1); para. 198, ll. 1–11 (pp. 415–16); para. 212, ll. 16–22 (pp. 425–6) and ll. 29–32 (p. 426); para. 216, ll. 1–7 (p. 427); para. 227, ll. 4–18 (p. 434); para. 89, ll. 1–19 (p. 343)).

[35] See Laslett (ed.), op. cit. 2nd Treatise, para. 99, ll. 1–5 (p. 351).

extent be voided by the wrong actions of the inheritor and in the same way the duties can to some extent be voided by the iniquities of the authority to which they are owed. But after the initial express consent which establishes the political community has been given, there no longer exists a set of rights unencumbered with contingent duties. It seems that here too it is a failure to take full account of the context in which Locke's arguments are set which leads Mr Plamenatz to misunderstand their bearing and to mistake their success.

If it is the question of the express consent which initiates political society that, in this way, misleads Mr Plamenatz, it seems to be a misconception of the express consent which makes an individual a full member of a society which misleads Professor Macpherson. He wishes to show that Locke made the propertyless into subjects of his class state but excluded them from full membership in it. It was, in his opinion, in order to carry out this unattractive project that Locke developed the distinction between a tacit and an express consent. The first category is employed because of the impossibility of demonstrating in any other way that the propertyless are subject to the laws of political society. With careful skill, it assimilates the situation of the propertyless in their own society, their rights and duties, to those of resident aliens. But *does* Locke's concept in fact do this? Macpherson's claim rests squarely on the proposition that 'the only men who are assumed to incorporate themselves in any commonwealth by express compact are those who have some property, or the expectation of some property in land'.[36] But the only evidence which he cites[37] for this interpretation will not bear the weight put upon it. In the passage cited Locke states that any man who makes himself a subject of political society in order to protect his property submits this to be regulated by the laws of the society. It is true that he takes land as the example of property with which to continue the exposition of the point at issue; and it seems likely that it was both empirically the case that he thought of land as paradigmatic for other forms of real property and dialecti-

---

[36] Macpherson, op. cit. pp. 194–271, esp. pp. 247–51.
[37] Laslett (ed.), op. cit. 2nd Treatise, para. 120, ll. 2–11 (p. 366). (Cited by Macpherson, op. cit. pp. 249–50.) '. . . every Man, when he, at first, incorporates himself into any Commonwealth, he, by his uniting himself thereunto, annexed also, and submits to the Community those Possessions, which he has, or shall acquire, that do not already belong to any other Government. For it would be a direct Contradiction, for any one, to enter into Society with others for the securing and regulating of Property; and yet to suppose his Land, whose Property is to be regulated by the Laws of the Society, should be exempt from the Jurisdiction of that Government, to which he himself the Proprietor of the Land, is a Subject.'

cally the case that land fits his argument here more neatly than movable property (most of all, money). But by any canons of interpretation the fact that he takes land as his example cannot in itself be taken to imply that he thought there were no other examples. The paragraph in question was not intended to give an exhaustive statement of the motives that might lead men to join a political society; it was designed to emphasize that property inside political societies can only be held subject to the rules of those societies.

Furthermore, even if Macpherson's inference was a permissible interpretation of the paragraph itself, it would still not have the implications he suggests. For the paragraph considers only the inception of political society and not the circumstances under which men may wish to incorporate themselves in the existing political societies in which their families have lived for centuries. To suppose that Locke would have considered the actual nature of their motivations under such vastly different circumstances as identical is absurd. To take the relationship about which Macpherson himself has been most emphatic; the fact that at the inception of political society there would have been no adult who did not own land (or, at least, could not do so if he wished), and hence no non-land-holding adult would have had reasons to incorporate himself into a political society, does not imply that in the maturity of political societies when there are many men born into their society without any property in land or the probability of acquiring it, such men could have no reason for incorporating themselves into their society. Thus, once it is noted, as it is by Macpherson himself,[38] that 'Not every proprietor of land is necessarily a full member of the society—foreigners and even natives who have not actually incorporated themselves in the society may possess land there', there ceases to be any reason to accept his conclusion that 'every full member is assumed to be a proprietor of land'. The problem then returns to where it is in the text of Locke himself—how is it in fact that men *do* incorporate themselves in society; just what sort of a performance *is* an 'express' or 'explicit' consent?

There is no very clear answer to this question and it is a damaging lacuna in Locke's theory that there should be none. At this point, at best, an account can be given of the sort of considerations which make his statements intelligible; no account of how the statements as they stand are consistent is possible because as they stand they do not make adequate sense. Professor Macpherson's attempt to resolve this

[38] Macpherson, op, cit. p. 250.

problem is ingenious but unconvincing, both in the detail examined above and in the general interpretation of Locke's position which it involves. The problem remains that Locke gives no instances of what he means by an express consent except that of a landowner previously in a state of nature who joins himself to a commonwealth. Can Locke really have meant that the only political societies in which all adult (male) inhabitants were members of the 'Body Politick' were ones which had only just been established and that the only members of the English 'Body Politick' in 1680 were naturalized property-holders? It is hard to believe this. It is hardly likely to be an accident that the example which Locke does give of men who were, over a period of time, 'subject to the laws' of a commonwealth, is of resident aliens.[39] It might be conceivable that he regarded those without property in England as enjoying a status identical to that of resident aliens; but it is scarcely credible that he should have extended this status to himself or to his patron, the great political magnate, the first Earl of Shaftesbury. Yet when had these two latter given a 'positive engagement, and express Promise and Compact'[40] to incorporate themselves into the realm of England? There are a number of occasions on which certain groups of people in seventeenth-century England were required to perform actions which could reasonably be described as giving positive engagements or making express promises or compacts *as* members of the society. The most notable of these was the requirement to take the oath of allegiance and supremacy.[41] Such oaths, for the most part, seem only to have been imposed upon public officeholders but it is clear that any member of the community was in principle liable to have them administered to him, if disaffection was prevalent and if a magistrate had any reason for doubting his loyalty.[42] Conceivably, by extension, the oath that a parish constable was required to take at his inception might have been regarded as a similar positive engagement.

---

[39] Laslett (ed.), op. cit. 2nd Treatise, para. 122, ll. 1–20; esp. ll. 12–16 (p. 367): ' . . . thus we see, that *Foreigners*, by living all their Lives under another Government, and enjoying the Priviledges and Protection of it, though they are bound, even in Conscience, to submit to its Administration, as far forth as any Denison; yet do not thereby come to be *Subjects or Members of that Commonwealth*.'

[40] Laslett (ed.), op. cit. 2nd Treatise, para. 122, ll. 17–18 (p. 367).

[41] For some of the occasions on which such an oath was administered and some idea of the sorts of persons to whom it would be administered, see e.g. K. Feiling, *A History of the Tory Party 1640–1714* (Oxford, 1924), pp. 262–6, 284–5, 319–21 and J. R. Western, *The English Militia in the Eighteenth Century* (London, 1965), pp. 33–4, 83.

[42] See e.g. Feiling, op. cit. pp. 284–5 and Western, op. cit. pp. 33–4.

However this does not get us much further. For these oaths are always taken as such by men who are already in any common sense understanding 'members of the society'.

To return to the passage quoted above (footnote 39), resident aliens are said not to be 'Subjects or Members' of the commonwealth in which they live, though 'subject to' the laws of England, they are not English 'Subjects'. But could it be true that Locke thought the huge mass of propertyless labourers were not English subjects? Or are there three categories involved—Members, Subjects, and those 'subject to the laws'? What would best make sense of these murky statements and is it likely that Locke believed what would best make sense of them? The simplest assumption, perhaps, would be that he thought of all natural-born Englishmen (who did not expressly decide, at some point close to the time at which they came of age, to emigrate) as members of the society; and that he thought of their express consent as a hypothetical event, like the express consent of the propertied, as the answer they would give if asked the question, 'Are you an Englishman, a subject of the King of England?'[43] For even if the large property-owner was more likely to proclaim his membership of the political society in a definite public act, through holding a public office like a justiceship of the peace or a lieutenancy of the militia, any adult male Englishman was just as much liable to have an oath administered to him, if his conduct gave reasons for suspicion.[44] To suppose that a suspected supporter of the Fifth Monarchist Venner who agreed to take the oath of allegiance would have thereby become a member of English society, while a rich landowner who had never held public office had not, is inconceivable. For all Locke's insistence on the explicitness of an express consent, it seems that what must be important is the disposition manifested by behaviour, rather than any specific occasion. Men must be supposed expressly to consent to their nationality, their membership in a given society, by their settled disposition to identify themselves as such (those who are not immigrants are, after all, seldom in doubt about their nationality). All this seems rather weak; but, I fear, the weakness is Locke's own and cannot readily be amended by substituting an extrinsic strength.

A further problem arises over the nature of an express consent. Those who are not full members of a society are stated to have a

---

[43] Cf. the example of 'countrymen' as a 'natural relation' in the *Essay concerning Human Understanding* (cited in footnote 27 above) and Laslett (ed.), op. cit. 2nd Treatise, para. 117, ll. 1–8 (p. 364).

[44] Western, op. cit. pp. 33–4.

natural right of emigration, though not of taking their property with them when they emigrate.[45] But this natural right to emigrate does not apply to the members of the political society.[46] In other words, at the point at which a man becomes a perfect member of a society he loses the right which he previously enjoyed to leave it at will. Locke gives no reason for this position—it is a consequence of the definition which he gives of membership in political society—and it seems not to have any function in the structure of the theory. There is no particular reason why he would have thought it right to prevent those emigrating who wished to do so, even if the political society which they wished to leave was in itself fully legitimate.[47] What the position implies is simply that no one who accepts voluntarily his membership in a political society can subsequently claim any *right* to leave it at will, if the political authorities of the society object to his doing so.

Once a man is inside political society the issue of consent arises again only over the taxation of property. Locke's discussion of property is designed precisely to remove the right to it from the historically inconceivable 'express Compact of all the Commoners[48] so successfully demolished by Filmer.[49] But, if the origin of property is independent of consent, its transfer can only be made by consent. Indeed, the definition of property is simply that '*without a Man's own*

---

[45] Laslett (ed.), op. cit. 2nd Treatise, para. 120, ll. 1–21 (p. 366); para. 121, ll. 1–9 (p. 367). Though Locke's phrasing is even vaguer than usual over this issue, it seems (esp. para. 120) to be his property in *land* which he cannot take with him—for obvious reasons—and not property in money or goods. He can sell the land (para. 121, l. 8) which would presumably only make sense if he could take the money with him. That is, a man may inherit property without political obligation but whilst he is actually exploiting it (and hence deriving benefits from the government of the country within which it is located) he is obliged to obey the laws of that country. Cf. also para. 118, ll. 1–25 (pp. 364–5).

[46] Laslett (ed.), op. cit. 2nd Treatise, para. 121, ll. 11–18 (p. 367): '. . . he, that has once, by actual Agreement, and any *express* Declaration, given his *Consent* to be of any Commonweal, is perpetually and indispensably obliged to be and remain unalterably a Subject to it, and can never be again in the liberty of the state of Nature; unless by any Calamity, the Government, he was under, comes to be dissolved; or else by some publick Act cuts him off from being any longer a member of it.' See also para. 122, ll. 6–10 (p. 367).

[47] If the society in question were the France of Louis XIV and the intending refugees were persecuted Huguenots, of course, he regarded their right of emigration as beyond question.

[48] Laslett (ed.), op. cit. 2nd Treatise, para. 25, ll. 16–19 (p. 304). 'I shall endeavour to shew, how Men might come to have a *property* in several parts of that which God gave to Mankind in common, and that without any express Compact of all the Commoners.' See also para. 28, ll. 11–24 (pp. 306–7); para. 29, ll. 1–5 (p. 307); para. 32, ll. 4–10 (pp. 308–9).

[49] Filmer, op. cit. pp. 203–4, 248, 266, 273–4.

consent it *cannot be taken from him*'.[50] This does not mean, as has been emphasized above, that a man can hold property in an actual political community without thereby incurring duties. A man has a right to his own property and he has a '*Right,* before any other Man, to *inherit,* with his Brethren, his Fathers Goods'.[51] But the exercise of this right, if a parent has been a member of a political society, is contingent on accepting the rules of the society. This is not because there is something imperfect about his right of inheritance; he *does* have a right of inheritance before all other men—it is because this right (like all other rights in Locke except that of self-preservation, a right which is also a duty) is a conditional and not an absolute right.[52] How is this right of the political society to regulate and articulate the property rights of individuals compatible with their right to do with it whatever they wish; how, for instance, is this compatible with the right of the state to raise taxes? Locke's answer again seems dimly inconsequential. The state as such has *no* right to raise taxes.[53] No tax can ever legitimately be demanded as a right by any sovereign; all taxes can only be specific gifts from particular subjects.

But, naturally, such a position is totally incredible. The puzzle is to be solved by invoking the constitutional notion of representation. Men choose deputies, representatives, to give their consent for them; if the legal structure of the society is such that there are no facilities for their choosing their representatives, or if the appointed machinery for choosing their representatives is interfered with,[54] no tax can have any legitimacy except that conferred upon it by the individual voluntary

[50] Laslett (ed.), op. cit. 2nd Treatise, para. 193, l. 9 (p. 413); and see para. 138, ll. 1–17 (pp. 378–9); para. 139, ll. 3–8 (p. 379); para. 140, ll. 6–11 (p. 380); and para. 192, ll. 23–7 (p. 412) '. . . their due property, which is so to be Proprietors of what they have, that no body can take away part of it without their own consent, without which, Men under any Government are not in the state of Freemen, but are direct Slaves under the Force of War.'

[51] Laslett (ed.), op. cit. 2nd Treatise, para. 190, ll. 1–4 (pp. 411–12).

[52] Laslett (ed.), op. cit. 2nd Treatise, para. 116, ll. 14–24 (p. 364); esp. '. . . any *act of the Father can no more give away the liberty of the Son,* than it can of any body else: He may indeed annex such Conditions to the Land, he enjoyed as a Subject of any Commonwealth, as may oblige his Son to be of that Community, if he will enjoy those Possessions which were his Fathers; because that Estate being his Fathers Property, he may dispose or settle it as he pleases.'

[53] Laslett (ed.), op. cit. 2nd Treatise, para. 138, ll. 1–17 (pp. 378–9); esp. '. . . it is a mistake to think, that the Supream or *Legislative Power* of any Commonwealth, can do what it will, and dispose of the Estates of the Subjects *arbitrarily,* or take any part of them at pleasure.' *N.B. any* part of them; see also para. 139, ll. 3–8 (p. 379).

[54] Laslett (ed.), op. cit. 2nd Treatise, para. 155, ll. 1–17 (pp. 388–9); para. 216, ll. 1–7 (p. 427); para. 222, ll. 1–62 (pp. 430–2).

acquiescence of the taxed. The duty to support the expenses of government in due proportion to the benefits received from it is a duty which can be enforced only when it is explicitly recognized as such by the man who owes it.[55] An air of massive bad faith hangs over this whole area of the argument. For what is necessary, finally, is not the (inconceivable) consent of each individual but the consent of the majority given by their representatives (see footnote 55 above), as conveniently alleged to exist in the proper practice of the English constitution and as undeniably ritualized in English political rhetoric for decades. But why should the consent of the majority suffice? The obvious suggestion, that this is the minimum decision-procedure constitutive of political society, that it is what a man consents to in becoming a member of a political society at all, will hardly suffice. For, if a *past* consent is adequate to ensure obligation, an absolute monarchy created by the consent of its members would have arbitrary power over the property of its subjects. It seems unlikely that Locke meant this. It cannot be because it does constitute *in fact* the agreement of all individuals that Locke takes the consent of the majority as its equivalent. There *is* an extraordinary elision between the consent of each property-holder and the consent of the majority of the representatives of the majority of the property-holders, as chosen according to the English franchise in the late seventeenth century. It seems implausible that Locke was altogether unaware of any such elision. Why should he have made it and how can it make sense?

Firstly; it must again be emphasized that the *Two Treatises of Government* is a very specifically directed book. Causally, the reason why Locke does not consider the possibility of the oppression of a minority by a majority, and hence does not denounce it, is simply that it is not relevant to the issue about which he *is* writing. What he is attacking is the exploitation of a huge majority by a small minority. Had there been operative French representative institutions, he would not have regarded the confiscation of the property of the Huguenots on account of their religious beliefs as being in any way less arbitrary because it was carried out as a result of the votes of the Estates, representing the enthusiastic consent of the majority of the French population. He uses the cant of English constitutionalism in this insouciant (not to say careless) manner, not because it guarantees an administration of spotless purity but because he considers one particular theory of the English constitution as likely to provide better ad-

---

[55] Laslett (ed.), op. cit. 2nd Treatise, para. 140, ll. 1–11 (p. 380).

ministration than others. What is in question is not Utopia but the most desirable political arrangements that Shaftesbury or William III might reasonably aspire to bring about. To attempt to extrapolate the Lockean Utopia from such unpromising materials is a sterile exercise and the results, by necessity, faintly ludicrous.

But why should the 'consent of the majority' have this favoured pragmatic status? At the formal level no suggestions are even offered—it seems an uneasy amalgam of the arguments for majority-consent as a minimum decision-procedure and of the *a priori* equality in moral rectitude or turpitude of all men, a simple axiom, *ceteris paribus*, more rather than less. This seems unexceptionable and useless—but then it is not how it is used. It is where it *is* used that its plausibility and its pragmatic quality are most readily seen. For it is not *any* set of representatives or deputies which can be trusted in this way to further the interests of those whom they represent.[56] Most governmental bodies are always liable to think of themselves as having distinct interests and to behave accordingly. They are all too frequently disposed to make inroads on the property of the subjects for their own benefit and without any justification.[57] However, 'This is not much to be fear'd in Governments where the *Legislative* consists, wholly or in part, in Assemblies which are variable, whose Members upon the Dissolution of the Assembly, are Subjects under the common Laws of their Country, equally with the rest'.[58] Men remain sinful. Government remains imperfect. In governments with elective assemblies like the English, arbitrary expropriation of property is less to be feared than it is in other governments which lack this incomparable advantage. Absolute power may normally be an acceptable form of political authority, if it is in practice confined to the requirements of military defence or within social structures as simple as the patriarchal family. But the appropriation of property, unlike military leadership, needs more persistent referenda, if it is to be prevented from arbitrary exercise. It is the combination of temptation with opportunity which makes a sovereign's right to tax without the 'consent' of his subjects into such a dangerous threat. A particular institution generates the dangers; these

---

[56] See Laslett (ed.), op. cit. 2nd Treatise, para. 88, ll. 8–18 (pp. 342–3 and below). Indeed the status of representative is contingent on the due exercise of its functions; see para. 151, ll. 15–26 (p. 386).

[57] Laslett (ed.), op. cit. 2nd Treatise, para. 138, ll. 21–31 (p. 379); para. 143, ll. 7–15 (p. 382).

[58] Laslett (ed.), op. cit. 2nd Treatise, para. 138, ll. 17–21 (p. 379) see also para. 143, ll. 15–23 (p. 382); para. 142, ll. 10–15 (p. 381).

are best alleviated by another institution. In an absolute monarchy any tax ever levied derives whatever legitimacy it has solely from the individual psychological attitude of each taxed subject at the particular point in time at which he is taxed. In a Parliamentary government like England's there is a definite decision-procedure which if it is operated without chicanery guarantees the consent of the majority of the taxed. We do not know whether Locke thought that this was the best conceivable political system. What we do know is that it is an institution and not a generator of autonomous moral values. In the last resort the criterion for the just exercise of *its* powers, too, is the axiom: 'the power of the Society, or Legislative constituted by them, can never be suppos'd to extend farther than the common good; but is oblig'd to secure every ones Property . . .'[59] The moral authority of *all* institutions is restricted by the maxim of rational choice.[60]

Consent, then, inside political societies is both the mode in which individuals acquire their political obligations and the institutional precondition for each man to feel a reasonable security in his own possessions. But it is also what creates political society in the first place and this may well seem more peculiar. It is not very remarkable to base a political theory on the fact that men do to some extent recognize the legitimacy of the societies in which they live. It is harder to see how such a recognition could precede in time the social matrix from which it derives. Here, surely, we have not only historical fantasy but logical error. But do we? Consent is an axiomatic precondition for the legitimacy of any political authority because men are naturally equal in their status as the property of God.[61] But the crucial term here is legitimacy, not precondition. For it is a precondition not for the existence of any society whatsoever but for the existence of a society with an authority which has a *right* to the obedience of its members. Locke shows a great, and a justified, impatience with the question of the historical authentication of consent as the basis of primitive government, not because he did not know more than Filmer about primitive

---

[59] Laslett (ed.), op. cit. 2nd Treatise, para. 131, ll. 8–10 (p. 371).

[60] Laslett (ed.), op. cit. 2nd Treatise, para. 131, ll. 6–8 (p. 371) ('For no rational Creature can be supposed to change his condition with an intention to be worse') and para. 164, ll. 1–2 (p. 395) etc.

[61] Laslett (ed.), op. cit. 2nd Treatise, para. 15, ll. 13–16 (p. 296); para. 22, ll. 1–8 (p. 301); para. 95, ll. 1–14 (pp. 348–9); para. 171, ll. 12–25 (p. 400); para. 175, ll. 1–13 (pp. 402–3); para. 176, ll. 28–31 (p. 404); para. 198, ll. 1–19 (pp. 415–16); para. 212, ll. 16–22 (pp. 425–6); para. 192, ll. 1–27 (p. 412); and references cited in footnote 16 above.

government[62] but because his argument is in no way contingent on the historical questions of how primitive governments did begin. All that is necessary for his argument, except in so far as its efficacy simply as propaganda is concerned, is that there should be *some* instances of men confronting each other in 'a state of nature', that is, outside any shared structure of positive law. (Strictly speaking not even this degree of evidence is necessary to the argument; but its expository cogency is undoubtedly much strengthened by it.) To establish this, the Swiss and Indian in the woods of America[63] are quite sufficient. The perfunctory pre-history of government which is from time to time invoked adds nothing to the theory and lends to it a degree of historical contingency which it clearly did not have in Locke's mind. The whole account is correspondingly obscure. There seem to be two historically substantial stages, an authentically primitive one and an advanced constitutional one; and the confusion seems to derive from the attempt to conflate the two. The first stage, patriarchal monarchy and military leadership in war time, is discussed as an example of political authority based upon consent; while at the same time it is clearly recognized to be devoid of 'known standing laws'.[64] Advanced political societies, like England, are (when their constitutional proprieties are not being infringed by the iniquities of their governors) characterized by 'known

[62] He was in fact one of the best informed students in the Europe of his time of variations in the moral, social, political, and religious practices of non-European countries, a fact which has led Laslett to observe that he 'may be said to have done more than anyone else to found the study of comparative anthropology' (Laslett (ed.), op. cit. p. 98 n.). Certainly he played a major role in the planning and assembling of material for the fine collection produced by his publisher John Churchill, in four folio volumes, in 1704 (*A Collection of Voyages & Travels in 4 Volumes* London, 1704). For the extent of his interests see: G. Bonno, 'Les Relations Intellectuelles de Locke avec la France', *University of California Publications in Modern Philology*, xxxviii, no. 2 (Berkeley, 1955), 37–264 (especially on Thévenot and Bernier); *John Locke's Travels in France 1675–9*, ed. John Lough (Cambridge, 1953); Correspondence in the Bodleian; Notebooks in the Bodleian; Journals in the Bodleian and British Museum (Add. MSS. 15642); Notes to *Essays on the Law of Nature*, ed. Von Leyden; *Essay concerning Human Understanding*, etc. For the works contained in his library see John Harrison and Peter Laslett, *The Library of John Locke* (Oxford, 1965). The total bulk is extremely impressive. I emphasize its existence to show how extended is the context in which Locke elaborates his 'political rationalism'.

[63] Laslett (ed.), op. cit. 2nd Treatise, para. 14, ll. 12–17 (p. 295).

[64] Laslett (ed.), op. cit. 2nd Treatise, para. 75, ll. 1–5 (p. 335); para. 76, ll. 1–2 (p. 336); paras. 105–12 (pp. 354–62); and 1st Treatise, paras. 130–2 (pp. 254–6); para. 153 (p. 272). Also *A Second Letter concerning Toleration, Works*, ii, 423; and *A Third Letter for Toleration, Works*, ii, 488. MSS. Locke, c. 33. fo. 11^r miscited by Laslett (ed.), op. cit. p. 356 n.

settled laws' and by a legislative process which is at least to a significant
extent controlled by elected 'deputies' of 'the People'. If government
normally begins as monarchy,[65] and if to change the legislative is to set
up a new government, there must have been some occasion in the past
at which each advanced society acquired its governmental form. One
may conjecture that this occasion normally resulted from previous
injustice, either on the part of an incumbent monarch[66] or on the part
of an alien conqueror.[67] In either case there must have been some
definite occasion on which the people, either in person or acting
through elected representatives, voluntarily recognized the legitimacy
of their government.[68]

It is clear what sort of occasion in English constitutional mythol-
ogy is being invoked here, though whether Locke thought of it as a
specific historical occasion or the authentic 'Ancient Constitution'
itself,[69] is obscure. It is equally clear what sort of circumstances could

[65] Laslett (ed.), op. cit. 2nd Treatise, para. 105, ll. 1–3 (p. 354); para. 106,
ll. 1–8 (p. 355).

[66] Laslett (ed.), op. cit. 2nd Treatise, para. 107 (pp. 356–7); paras. 110–11
(pp. 359–61); para. 162 (p. 394); and for its application to the history of England,
paras. 165–6 (pp. 395–6).

[67] Laslett (ed.), op. cit. 2nd Treatise, para. 175, ll. 9–13 (p. 403); '*Conquest*
is as far from setting up any Government, as demolishing an House is from building a new one in the place. Indeed it often makes way for a new Frame of a
Common-wealth, by destroying the former; but, without the Consent of the
people, can ever erect a new one.'

[68] Laslett (ed.), op. cit. 2nd Treatise, para. 192, ll. 17–25 (p. 412): '. . . no
Government can have a right to obedience from a people who have not freely
consented to it; which they can never be supposed to do, till either they are put in
a full state of Liberty to chuse their Government and Governors, or at least till
they have such standing Laws, to which they have by themselves or their Representatives, given their free consent, and also till they are allowed their due
property, which is so to be Proprietors of what they have, that nobody can take
away any part of it without their own consent', and see para. 176, ll. 26–31 (p.
404); para. 198, ll. 11–19 (p. 416).

[69] See John Pocock, *The Ancient Constitution and the Feudal Law* (Cambridge, 1957); also J. W. Gough, *Fundamental Law in English Constitutional
History* (Oxford, 1955); David Douglas, *English Scholars 1660–1740* (London,
1951); Christopher Hill, *Puritanism and Revolution* (c. 3 'The Norman Yoke')
(London, 1958). S. Kliger, *The Goths in England* (Cambridge, Mass., 1952) and
an important article by Quentin Skinner, 'History and Ideology in the English
Revolution,' *Historical Journal*, VIII, no. 2 (1965), 151–78, for the nature of the disputes about the historicity of the 'Ancient Constitution'. Locke himself seems
always to have shown a judicious lack of interest in the details of the dispute—
unless, that is, the missing portion of the *Two Treatises* contained such material,
a hypothesis for which there is really no evidence; but his letter to Edward Clarke
(cited in footnote 22 above) suggests that it is the authentic 'ancient constitution'
that he has in mind.

not be considered as instances of the institution of governments by consent. Conquest was one of the favoured accounts for the origins of the English constitution (favoured, for obvious reasons, only by those who wished to give an absolutist interpretation of that constitution). Though, in its historiographical form, the Norman Yoke, it hardly enters the purview of Locke's argument as this survives, in the less historically contingent form of unrecorded past usurpation, it is a frequent theme of Filmer's (as of Hobbes's and most other absolutist theorists of the period). Indeed it played the role of an absolutist historico-legal fiction in a manner closely analogous to the Whig historico-legal fiction of the contract. The rejection of conquest as a basis for political legitimacy, and the distinction between consent and submission by which this rejection is carried out, are the most unequivocal indications of what sort of purchase his notion of consent was intended to have upon concrete social situations. It is thus far from surprising that the only piece of writing after the publication of the *Two Treatises* itself which indicates a renewal of Locke's interests in the problem of the grounds of political duties should focus upon the issue of the legitimacy of a usurping regime. In the notes which he wrote out on William Sherlock's *Case of Allegiance* he confronted a theory even more crudely Panglossian than that of Filmer.[70]

Sherlock maintained that all social events of any complexity are a dispensation of divine providence, their causation a result of the subtle deflections by the deity of men's corrupt motives. To Locke, this seemed abject superstition in general and morally corrupt in particular. To assert, as Sherlock did,[71] that 'The Revolutions of Governments are not the Subjects Duty, but God's Prerogative' was simply grotesque. Furthermore, it made right a simple function of power. It meant that majorities, even rebellious majorities, must axiomatically be in the right.[72] Above all it destroyed the very notion of legitimacy and reduced to nullity any tolerable definition of the political relation-

---

[70] Notes on William Sherlock, *The Case of Allegiance Due to Sovereign Powers* (London, 1691). MSS. Locke, c. 28, fos. 83–96. No very searching treatment of Sherlock exists but see Gerald. M. Straka, 'The Final Phase of Divine Right Theory in England, 1688–1702', *English Historical Review* (1962), pp. 638–58; and more extendedly in his *The Anglican Reaction to the Revolution of 1688* (Madison, Wisconsin, 1962).

[71] Sherlock, op. cit. p. 43.

[72] Sherlock notes, MSS. Locke, c. 28, fo. 92^v: 'If rebels be the minority they may be fought against, if the majority they are our country and must not be fought against.' Cf. the discussion on the status of majority-consent above, footnote 34 and p. 148.

ship.[73] It assimilated submission wholly to consent. But a general submission is not the same as a general consent.[74] It may often serve as an indicator of such a consent; but in itself it does not constitute consent at all. Neither particular verbal performances nor coerced behavioural acquiescence suffice. What is necessary is *choice*.[75] The Greek Christians, hence, have a continuing right of resistance to their Turkish masters. They have never chosen the framework of government under which they live; and they are treated by their rulers in a manner which could only be permissible if they were 'slaves under the force of war', a situation which cannot even in principle last beyond a single generation.[76] What makes the critical difference is the absence of compulsion and the existence of choice.[77] Of these two, it is the absence of compulsion which comes closest to being a simple behavioural criterion. Choice is not seen as a particular historical event in the mind of the subject. Rather, the absence of compulsion is a necessary condition for the existence of choice. Certain behaviour in a particular context implies choice.[78] But if the behaviour is caused by external force, then it does not imply choice. This is certainly not a trivial criterion—it is because the 'noise of War . . . makes so great a part of the History of Mankind' that men have made the error of mistaking the force of arms, for the consent of the People.[79] It is precisely the

---

[73] Sherlock notes, MSS. Locke, c. 28, fos. 83–96 *passim* and esp. the comment on Sherlock's claim that the 'settlement' of a government gave it political authority (fo. 96ʳ). 'How long a month a year —or an hundred & by what rule what law of God. Long and short in such cases unless defined have no meaning people submit where they do not resist so that where there is no resistance there is a general submission, but there may be a general submission without a general consent which is an other thing.' Cf. Plamenatz, *Consent, Freedom, and Political Obligation*, p. 7, etc.

[74] See Sherlock notes MSS. Locke, c. 28 fo. 96ʳ.

[75] Laslett (ed.), op. cit. 2nd Treatise, para. 189, ll. 5–12 (p. 411): '. . . the Absolute Power of the *Conquerour* reaches no farther than the Persons of the Men, that were subdued by him, and dies with them; and should he govern them as Slaves, subjected to his Absolute, Arbitrary Power, he *has no* such *Right of Dominion over their Children*. He can have no Power over them, but by their own consent, whatever he may drive them to say, or do; and he has no lawful Authority, whilst Force, and not Choice, compels them to submission.' And see para. 186, ll. 1–22 (pp. 410–11).

[76] Laslett (ed.), op. cit. 2nd Treatise, para. 179, ll. 1–8 (p. 406); para. 186, ll. 1–22 (pp. 410–11); para. 189, ll. 2–12 (p. 411); para. 192, ll. 1–27 (p. 412); para. 176, ll. 26–31 (p. 404).

[77] Laslett (ed.), op. cit. 2nd Treatise, para. 189, ll. 11–12 (p. 411); para. 186, ll. 1–22 (pp. 410–11); para. 192, ll. 1–14, and ll. 19–22 (p. 412).

[78] This is plainly not a philosophical analysis of what it is to choose; simply a substantive moral rule about what may be counted by others as a choice.

[79] Laslett (ed.), op. cit. para. 175, ll. 1–13, pp. 402–3.

hideous preponderance of force in human history and the sycophantic ideologies which this has generated, which it is the purpose of Locke's political theory to confront and to expose.

But the confrontation is not achieved by turning the entire weight of the legitimate social order upon the shifting consciousnesses of individuals at arbitrarily selected points in time. Such a conception would indeed be democratic, not to say anarchic; and, if Locke were to predicate such a claim of the English political community in his day, he could have done so only in the most radical bad faith. The legitimacy of the polity could no more be solely a construct out of such psychological contingency than the moral order itself. The exaggeratedly individualist and voluntarist character of such a theory would deprive every existing polity of its legitimacy. To follow why Locke did not see it as having this result, it is necessary to understand the structure of ideas within which it is to be interpreted. To see why it is that Locke should have adopted so early and held with such little strain the queasy historical fiction that governments have originated from the consent of the people,[80] it is necessary to take note of the assumed sociology which underlies his argument and the criteria for rational choice and legal authority which are embedded in it. The most central assumption of his political theory, the irrelevance of history, was not an easy theme to bring to bear on the relentless legalism of English political discourse in the seventeenth century. Indeed, it was such a difficult task to do so that much of our own critical literature on Locke has significantly failed to grasp it. The strenuous attempt by Professor Richard Cox, for instance, to decode the true meaning of the Lockean doctrine from the 'real' empirical character of the 'state of nature' is only the most single-minded of such enterprises.[81] To a greater or lesser extent this misunderstanding seems still to colour most of our interpretations. In the remainder of this paper, I shall argue that it is the continuity of reason and the general human propensity to accept even minimally legitimate hierarchies of authority which best define Locke's theory and which lead him to his characteristic insouciance before the contingencies of history. Finally, I shall attempt a brief and

---

[80] Abrams (ed.), op. cit. pp. 124, 125, 126, 128, 129, 130, 138, 150, 172, 200–1 (230–1). These references seem all to be hypothetical, though cf. Abrams (ed.), op. cit. pp. 25–27, 75, 76, 78 (and esp. deleted passage at p. 172), for the claim that the hypothesis is essential to the form of Locke's argument.

[81] Richard H. Cox, *Locke on War and Peace* (Oxford, 1960), chs. I and II esp. For a general critique of the defects in Cox's lines of argument, see J. W. Yolton. 'Locke on the Law of Nature,' *Philosophical Review,* October 1958.

somewhat more formal summary of the nature of his conception of consent.

The role of reason in the definition of the contours of consent alters to some extent from one stage of social development to another. Initially, whatever a man 'actually consents to' is licit,[82] unless it is in itself something which he does not have the authority to consent to— i.e. it is in itself an action which it could never be licit for him to perform. Thereafter, whatever a man has acted in such a way as to make himself responsible for, he may be said to have consented to, and reason enters the relationship only as the criterion of what sort of action constitutes making himself responsible for what other sort of action. Reason implies, for instance, that the legitimate exercise of any authority must be limited to the pursuit of the ends which the authority may be held to serve. These ends are known by a process of rational enquiry (in principle), by knowledge of the law of nature.[83] A more specific instance of this position is that the authority derived by a political society from the consent of its subjects is limited to acts which it is in the general interest of the subjects to empower.[84] Still more restrictively, where the actions of the political authorities, even in a perfectly legitimate polity, are in themselves vicious, the subjects cannot be held responsible for them unless they have directly expe-

---

[82] Laslett (ed.), op. cit. 2nd Treatise, para. 97, ll. 8–14 (p. 350): 'For what appearance would there be of any Compact? What new Engagement if he were no farther tied by any Decrees of the Society, than he himself thought fit, and did actually consent to? This would be still as great a liberty as he himself had before his Compact, or any one else in the State of Nature hath, who may submit himself and consent to any acts of it if he thinks fit.'

[83] Laslett (ed.), op. cit. 2nd Treatise, para. 222, ll. 40–6 (p. 431): 'For the People having reserved to themselves the Choice of their *Representatives*, as the Fence to their Properties, could do it for no other end, but that they might always be freely chosen and so chosen, freely act and advise, as the necessity of the Commonwealth, and the publick Good should, upon examination, and mature debate, be judged to require.' See also para. 17, ll. 4–16 (p. 297); para. 139, ll. 9–11 (p. 379): '. . . even *absolute Power*, where it is necessary, is *not Arbitrary* by being absolute, but is limited by that reason, and confined to those ends, which required it in some Cases to be absolute . . .', and more generally para. 104, ll. 1–7 (p. 354); para. 118, ll. 11–13 (p. 365) and the form of the argument in para. 120, ll. 1–21 (esp. l. 6) (p. 366).

[84] Laslett (ed.), op. cit. 2nd Treatise, para. 164, ll. 1–19 (esp. ll. 1–9), (p. 395): 'But since a Rational Creature cannot be supposed when free, to put himself into Subjection to another, for his own harm: (Though where he finds a good and wise Ruler, he may not perhaps think it either necessary, or useful to set precise Bounds to his Power in all things) *Prerogative* can be nothing, but the Peoples permitting their Rulers, to do several things of their own free choice, where the law was silent, and sometimes too against the direct Letter of the Law, for the publick good; and their acquiescence in it when so done.'

dited them.[85] On the other hand, particular exercises of authority to which the people have not yet specifically consented or which are in direct conflict with the structure of rules to which the people have consented may be considered to carry the consent of the people where they clearly further the ends for which the rules were originally established.[86] All these examples have one feature in common. They are all instances of rational interpretations of the nature of consents given by a people within a legitimate society. The question of the rational criteria for originating a legitimate political society is never faced very firmly; but the position implied is clear enough. What constitutes the legitimacy of a political society is precisely its recognition as legitimate by its subjects.[87] The issue of just what such a recognition would be like as an event in the world is not discussed because it had happened long enough ago in England for its precise historical character to be irrelevant. But the formal nature of the claim is clear—it is the recognition of legitimacy which creates the legitimacy of the sovereign.[88] It would seem more natural, perhaps, today to put this as the recognition *constituting* rather than creating the legitimacy; but, when taken with Locke's account of revolutionary right, his analysis of legitimacy seems markedly similar to that recently favoured by Professor Hare.[89]

[85] Laslett (ed.), op. cit. 2nd Treatise, para. 179, ll. 1–12 (p. 406): '. . . the *Conquerour* gets no Power but only over those, who have actually assisted, concurr'd, or consented to that unjust force, that is used against him. For the People having given to their Governours no Power to do an unjust thing, such as to make an unjust War, (for they never had such a Power in themselves): They ought not to be charged, as guilty of the Violence and Unjustice that is committed in an Unjust War, any farther, than they actually abet it; no more, than they are to be thought guilty of any Violence or Oppression their Governours should use upon the People themselves, or any part of their Fellow Subjects, they having impowered them no more to the one, than to the other.'

[86] Laslett (ed.), op. cit. 2nd Treatise, para. 158, ll. 1–39 (pp. 391–2) (esp. ll. 12–16): '. . . it being the interest, as well as the intention of the People, to have a fair and *equal* Representative; whoever brings it nearest to that, is an undoubted Friend, to, and Establisher of the Government, and cannot miss the Consent and Approbation of the Community.' See also ch. xiv 'Of Prerogative,' pp. 392–8, *passim.*

[87] Laslett (ed.), op. cit. 2nd Treatise, para. 192, ll. 1–27 (p. 412) and see footnote 68 above.

[88] More abstractly, for those who are members of a particular political society (the vagueness is present in Locke; but does it damage the argument?) there is a primary sense in which to predicate legitimacy of its authorities has a crucial illocutionary force which is more than simply descriptive. See J. L. Austin, *How to do things with Words* (Oxford, 1962).

[89] Cf. R. M. Hare, 'The Lawful Government,' in Peter Laslett and W. G. Runciman, *Philosophy, Politics, and Society,* 3rd Series (Oxford, 1967).

Of course, in context and intention it is radically different; I emphasize the resemblance in detail merely to make the exposition a little more intelligible.

Locke's expectations about the viability of social authority are nowhere systematically expressed. To complicate the matter further, the point at which they are voiced most explicitly in the *Two Treatises* is one at which he might well be suspected of disingenuousness. Even if, as I think probable, the position there stated is wholly sincere (however great the change may seem from his anxieties of 1660 and the *Tracts on Government*), what it asserts is more the behavioural inertness of the people than its normative acceptance of the legitimacy of authority.[90] This sense of voluntary moral acquiescence is less spelled out; but it is often invoked. In the discussions of prerogative and of the patriarchal origins of political authority[91] as in the incidental assumptions about the efficacy of social order,[92] it is a continuing theme. The phrase which perhaps best summarizes the notion is 'voluntary assent and acquiescence'. There is nothing very creative about such a response. Where authority is legitimate, it is both a simple duty and a natural inclination to acquiesce in it.

There is an illuminating analogy between the way in which Locke talks of consenting to authority in this way and his conception of assenting to the truth of beliefs about the world.[93] Occasionally he even uses consent and assent interchangeably. The notion of a truth is

---

[90] See Laslett (ed.), op. cit. 2nd Treatise, paras. 208, 209, 223, 225, 230 etc. and cf. Locke, *Some Considerations of the Consequences of the Lowering of Interest. . . . Works*, II, 46. It is only in conditions of acute scarcity, and normally only as a result of maladministration that members of the working classes attempt to act as an economic pressure group; but it seems to be also only at such a time that Locke expects them to 'forget respect'.

[91] Laslett (ed.), op. cit. 2nd Treatise, chs. XIV and VIII, esp. para. 105, ll. 8–16, 24–29 (pp. 354–5); para. 112, ll. 1–8 (p. 361); para. 74, ll. 10–37 (pp. 334–5); para. 75, ll. 1–5 (p. 335) ('Thus 'twas easie, and almost natural for Children by a tacit, and scarce avoidable consent to make way for the *Father's* Authority and Government. They had been accustomed in their Childhood to follow his Direction, and to refer their little differences to him, and when they were Men, who fitter to rule them?'); para. 76, ll. 1–2 (p. 336) ('by an insensible change'). Besides above on patriarchal origins see, on prerogative, esp. para. 94, ll. 10–17 (p. 347); para. 158, ll. 12–16 (p. 391); paras. 161, 162 (pp. 393–4).

[92] See footnotes 90 and 91 above; e.g., Locke, *Some Thoughts concerning Education. . . . Works*, IV, Preface, side 2 (not paginated). '. . . that most to be taken care of, is the gentleman's calling. For if those of that rank are by their education once set right, they will quickly bring all the rest into order.'

[93] See *Hum. Und. passim* (e.g. I, 6, 10, 12, 14, 15, 16, 22, 39, etc.) and see Draft A of the *Essay* (ed. Aaron and Gibb); Draft B (ed. Rand), etc.

not contingent on whether individuals *do* assent to it[94]—but the only way in which it can be known to be true is in such an assent. Men have a responsibility to 'regulate' their assent; they have cognitive duties[95] and they have a duty not to assent to false ideas. There is an order of potentially recognized legitimacy and potentially apprehended truth; the order of nature. There are also orders of authorized legitimate governments and systematically apprehended truths: the orders of political society and of Science. These latter are frailer and more contingent in appearance; and because Locke is concerned so sharply with epistemology, it seems often in his writing as if they are all there is. But this is to take a methodological empiricism and voluntarism for an ontological one. It is their reluctance to admit the degree of intellectual disorder which he displays here that has misled commentators into wishing a more elegant theory upon him.

What, then, is the role of consent in the theory of the *Two Treatises?* And what are the criteria for its existence in the world? For one to be said to have consented to a practice there are the following necessary conditions: (1) The occasion on which one is said to have consented must have been one on which one was acting voluntarily— that is to say that the claim that an act displays consent is defeasible by the demonstration that it was directly coerced; consent is not the same as submission. But to act voluntarily does not imply to act without powerful motivations[96]—it is precisely because there are such compel-

---

[94] In this respect it is plainly stricter than its political analogue. Consent is a necessary condition for a legitimate political society. No human psychological state can be a necessary condition for a notion being true. However it seems very likely that Locke would have held that men living in a non-political context in a complex society had a duty to confer political legitimacy upon that society by their consents. Plainly such a notion is quite irrelevant to the theme of the *Two Treatises* itself; but it was far from irrelevant to its subsequent polemical career. Some such assumption seems to make better sense of the embarrassing situation in which Locke was placed by his friend William Molyneux's invocation of his authority in defence of the English ascendancy in Ireland in the latter's *The Case of Ireland's being Bound by Acts of Parliament in England* (Dublin, 1698) and the extensive debate which this evoked.

[95] Cf. the development of the suicide taboo argument in more radical eighteenth-century writers into the specific *duty* to resist arbitrary power—e.g. Jonathan Mayhew, *A Discourse concerning Unlimited Submission and Non-resistance to the Higher Powers* (Boston, 1750), conveniently in Bernard Bailyn (and Jane N. Garrett), *Pamphlets of the American Revolution: 1750–1776* (Cambridge, Mass., 1965) (with excellent introduction), I, 203–47.

[96] See *Hum. Und.* I, 219: 'He that has his chains knocked off and the prison doors set open to him is perfectly at *liberty*, because he may either go or stay as he best likes, though his preference be determined to stay by the darkness of the night or illness of the weather or want of other lodging. He ceases not to be free,

ling economic reasons for any man to remain in his country of birth
that he is so clearly obliged to consent to its government, if legitimate.
(2) Nor does it mean to choose explicitly and self-consciously to
accept the practice—this is 'express' or 'explicit' consent. (And even
'express' consent does not depend upon having any reasonable future
grasp of the probable consequences of accepting the practice.)[97]
What the occasion must be is one which indicates a *prima facie* disposition to take (normally, presumably indefinite) advantage of the
practice. (3) The practice must be legitimate in itself.[98] This latter is
the most complex criterion. It is also probably the most important. It
explains why the fact that the Greek Christians do not emigrate (and
the fact that they presumably use such roads and other utilities and
administrative facilities as the Turkish regime provides) in no way
enhances the legitimacy of the Turkish regime. In these terms most
governments in the world of his day must have seemed to Locke of
highly dubious legitimacy. It explains why not deserting the territory
of a monarch who starts an unjust war does not make one guilty of
waging unjust war oneself. In other words, to summarize, where a
practice is legitimate and a role involves participation in the practice,
consent to doing so and hence consent to its responsibilities is axio-

---

though the desire of some convenience to be had there absolutely determines his
preference and makes him stay in his prison.' This passage seems closely to parallel
the implications of his discussion of the right of emigration, a notion which plays
an essential role in his theory.

[97] See the discussion in ch. v of the *Two Treatises* of the origins of large
differentials in property-holdings through the (necessarily consensual) development of a money economy. Cf. for a clear statement, John Rawls, 'Justice as Fair-
ness', in Peter Laslett and W. G. Runciman, *Philosophy, Politics, and Society*, 2nd
Series (Oxford, 1962)—though it seems important to point out that in the world
as it is some people always *do* have less deft senses of their probable future situation within a 'practice' than others—and that these differences in predictive skills
seem highly correlated with class differentials.

[98] I.e. it must itself have been formally legitimate in the past (where a popu-
lace in a state of nature fails to set up a political authority by its consent, all
individual members of it might be said to be morally at fault but no existing locus
of power would necessarily acquire any authority over them because of this).
This is the most equivocal issue (and the only one about which an enquiry like
W. Kendall's makes sense). The most essential premise, as said above, is the
ideological viability of hierarchy. The problem as Locke sees it is not that men are
not prone to accept legitimate hierarchies, but that they are all too prone to accept
illegitimate ones. But their acceptance and sanctioning of such hierarchies cannot
be construed to their disadvantage in particular cases except when it is specific
to those cases. The only act which can be *construed* to one's disadvantage is the
voluntary exploitation of a practice—and that only when one has broken the
rules which define the practice.

matic—all potential doubts are resolved in favour of the practice. But when it is illegitimate the doubts are resolved in favour of the agent. In the last resort the judge of the legitimacy of a practice can only be God. The terrestrial consequences may not reveal his judgement of the act; but the eternal ones will do so, just as they will reveal his judgement of every other human act.

Locke has sometimes been accused of propounding a sort of political solipsism. It is easy to see how a theory which bases political obligation upon consent might be open to such a charge.[99] But no such hubris does in fact dominate Locke's vision of politics. The shells which men have built for their shelter in the conduct of their social life are frail and impermanent; the responsibilities which they bear are heavy and the dangers which threaten them incessant. All the best and all the worst which they represent is a product of the shifting struggle in every human conscience of reason and passion, good and evil. In this unedifying drama the consent of men, as I have tried to show, is merely the mode in which political authority acquires such legitimacy as it has. But legitimacy is no final and irrevocable achievement. Human life is always a broken-backed affair, whose sole sufficient rationale must remain in another world than this. Such a theory provides a bizarre starting point indeed for the investigation of any topic in contemporary political theory. Can either be much illuminated by so odd a tactic?[100]

[99] Since the completion of this article Hanna Pitkin has treated Locke's theory of consent in an article, 'Obligation and Consent', *American Political Science Review*, LIX, no. 4 (Dec. 1965), 990–9 and LX, no. 1 (March, 1966), 39–52. See esp. pp. 994–7. While I do not at all agree with the general argument of the article and consider the framework within which Locke's concept is analysed as importantly misleading, the account of the structure of the concept seems to me unusually lucid, perceptive, and just.

[100] I should like to acknowledge the kindness of Mr Peter Laslett and Mr Quentin Skinner in reading this article for me and in making numerous helpful comments on it.

AUTHORITY AND THE RIGHTS OF INDIVIDUALS*

Richard I. Aaron

What constitution is best fitted for a free people? Of the three forms, democracy, oligarchy, and monarchy, Locke felt that none was wholly satisfactory in itself, and he favoured a mixed constitution, namely, the constitutional or limited monarchy, which the Whigs were then establishing. In accordance with this constitution, the people elect the legislative assembly and grant it the 'legislative power', that is, 'the power . . . to direct how the force of the commonwealth shall be employed for preserving the community and the members of it'.[1] In the main, this direction will take the form of legislation, although apparently it need not always do so. Next, there is the 'executive', 'to see to the execution of the laws that are made'.[2] As Locke explains the functions of this office it becomes clear that it contains both the judiciary and the executive in the modern sense, and it would have been well if he had distinguished between these offices. But he does not do so. The 'executive power', in Locke's sense, is usually placed in the hands of a single person, that is, the monarch. Finally, Locke introduces the 'federative', the name he gives to the office which concerns itself with foreign affairs. Locke finds that the federative and executive offices are usually united in the same person, that of the monarch, and he thinks this to be the wiser course. But on the whole he prefers to see the legislative and executive powers in separate hands. He is not perhaps as zealous for this separation as some have made out. But he does bring forward two arguments in favour of the separation of powers. First, as long as government continues in being the executive must be in being, but the legislative need sit only whilst it legislates and this is unlikely to take up the whole time of the members of the assembly. Secondly, a

* Reprinted from Richard I. Aaron, *John Locke*, 2nd ed. (Oxford, 1955), pp. 280–286, by permission of the Clarendon Press, Oxford.
[1] *Second Treatise*, § 143. Unless otherwise indicated, all references are to this work, designated only by section number.
[2] § 144.

more important argument: 'it may be too great temptation to human frailty, apt to grasp at power, for the same persons who have the power of making laws to have also in their hands the power to execute them.'[3] For these reasons Locke thinks that 'in all moderated monarchies and well-framed governments . . . the legislative and executive power are in distinct hands'.[4]

A question of considerable difficulty which now arises is that as to sovereignty. Who is sovereign in Locke's state? The monarch, having executive and federative powers, is none the less responsible to the legislative. Accordingly he is not supreme, except in a secondary sense. But the legislative again is responsible to the people and can be dismissed by the people. No doubt, the proper answer to the question is that the people are sovereign—although this answer would be clearer if we knew more precisely whom we are to understand by the term 'the people'. Once the legislative is appointed, however, and a government comes into being the sovereignty passes from the hands of the people into those of the legislative. The supremacy of the legislative while in session is a point which Locke stresses. Moreover, the monarch, the chief executive officer, also shares in the sovereignty. He has the right to dissolve the legislative assembly and possesses other prerogative powers which make him, on occasion at least, truly sovereign. Consequently, Locke's political theory is devoid of any clear-cut theory of sovereignty. In this respect it compares unfavourably with Hobbes's. In the *Leviathan* there is no doubting the identity of the sovereign; it is the absolute ruler. All the power of the state resides in him. Hobbes's theory is the more definite and logical and in that sense the more satisfying to the intellect. Yet it is logical at a price. It involves absolutism. Locke's problem is to find a constitution for a community which is determined to remain free, determined to avoid tyranny in any form. And he puts forward this system of check and countercheck wherein those who possess authority are limited in their powers and are throughout responsible for their actions.

As long as it sits 'the legislative is the supreme power . . . and all other powers in any members or parts of the society derived from and subordinate to it'.[5] 'In a very tolerable sense' the monarch also may be called supreme. He is the supreme executive and supreme federative officer of the state. But in both respects he is answerable to the legisla-

---

[3] § 143.
[4] § 159.
[5] § 150.

tive body. Other minor officers, of whom of course there must be many, 'are all of them accountable to some other power in the commonwealth'.[6] If, however, the government ceases to exist and is dissolved this does not mean the dissolution of the political society. It means that the sovereignty has returned to its original source, the people, who have the right and the power to set up a new legislative and executive. It is in this sense that 'the community perpetually retains a supreme power'.[7]

In this way Locke secures what he most strongly desires. If either the legislative body or, as Locke thinks more likely, the monarch, usurps its or his power in any way, then the people have a right to withdraw their support and to dissolve the government. Locke recognizes that the monarch has certain privileges. In a constitution of the kind sketched by him it will be necessary to leave many matters to the discretion of the chief executive officer. 'This power to act according to discretion for the public good, without the prescription of the law and sometimes even against it, is that which is called prerogative.'[8] Locke admits prerogative as necessary for the proper functioning of the governmental system. It is part of the king's prerogative also to dissolve the legislative and to assemble it when he thinks this will best serve the interest of the public. But if a monarch seeks to rule without the legislative body, if he interferes with its work and liberty, if he changes the method of electing the legislative without the consent of the people, if he 'delivers the people into the subjection of a foreign power', or, lastly, if he so neglects his executive duties as to cause the country to fall into a state of anarchy, then the people have a right to dismiss him. A monarch (or any other person) who seeks to become tyrant and to take absolute powers upon himself threatens the inner harmony of the society. He has put himself into a state of war with the people, and the people have a right to use force against him in order to rid themselves of him. Locke was not blind to the horrors of war. He particularly disliked the adulation paid to military men. 'We are apt to make butchery and rapine the chief marks and very essence of human greatness.'[9] And yet he could not bring himself to renounce war. Force must be met by force, lest the innocent should suffer for ever.

---

[6] § 149.
[7] Ibid.
[8] § 160.
[9] *Of Study*, in Lord King, *The Life of John Locke*, 2nd ed., 2 vols. (London, 1830), I, 178–179; cf. *Some Thoughts concerning Education* (London, 1693), pp. 53–54.

And a people have a right to use force if necessary against their ruler. Locke admits the right of rebellion. He here touches on what had been for some time a thorny problem. Even the more radical thinkers had hesitated before ascribing this right to the people. But Locke does not hesitate. The people, being always the supreme authority in any state, have a right to depose; it is their sacred duty to overthrow any individual who seeks to make his power over them absolute and despotic. To the objection that this will make for unsettled government Locke answers that the people are usually very loath to rebel, that they will suffer much before they resort to force. But there are limits to their patience. What is of vital importance is that they should always retain their supremacy and sovereignty in the state. To retain this, rebellion is justified.[10]

Such is the political doctrine which Locke sets forward in his second treatise. It is not free from defects. Locke is not thorough and does not exhaust his topic. He is too ready to set down general principles without considering all their implications. He neglects the details and brushes aside without sufficient consideration, or wholly neglects, many difficulties. Moreover, it cannot be denied that he deals too frequently in artificialities. His individual is artificial. He has no family ties. He tends to be conceived as a somewhat isolated being even when he enters into social relations with others. So also Locke's state is artificial. It is a community of free and independent individuals bound together by a compact into which they have entered freely for the better security of their lives, liberties, and estates—and it is nothing more. But surely a political or civil society is much more. For instance, Locke omits all reference to family and race. Racial or tribal sentiment, he thinks, may be neglected in discussing the origin of civil society. And yet to neglect race in this way is to commit as serious an error as is committed by those who see in a political society merely a racial group and who hold that race alone matters. Both views are artificial and over-simplified.

I may mention one further, and still more radical, defect. Locke is an individualist; yet his individualism is left undefined, for no definite solution is to be found in his works of the vexed problem of the relations between individual and community. There is one brand of individualism which can hardly be attributed to him, namely, that which would permit the individual complete licence. Locke's indi-

---

[10] Locke does not consider the possible effectiveness of constitutional amendment without rebellion.

vidual is never free without limitations. Even in the state of nature he
is a rational being and so knows, even though he may disobey, the law
of nature. And if he does disobey, other men punish him, so that an
element of compulsion enters. In civil society he is bound by a positive
legal code. Thus he is not free to do whatever he desires to do. None
the less, we are not to suppose that his freedom is necessarily curtailed
because he obeys the law. At least from the point of view of the more
rationalist side of Locke's moral and political teaching, obedience to
law is not bondage. Reason knows the law and delights in obeying it.
This point is not altogether explicit in Locke, but in a tentative way it
is present. To be rational is to know law, and to live under the law is to
live the free life. 'Freedom of men under government is to have a
standing rule to live by, common to everyone of that society and made
by the legislative power erected in it, a liberty to follow my own will
in all things where that rule prescribes not; and not to be subject to the
inconstant, uncertain, unknown, arbitrary will of another man: as
freedom of nature is to be under no other restraint but the law of
nature.'[11] The individual is free in spite of certain restraints upon
him.

   This point is clear. But the defect in Locke's position is that he
does not discuss the case of the individual who, for one reason or
another, finds the restraints imposed upon him by the community
unjust, a violation of what he conceives to be his individual rights.
What if the dictates of a man's conscience and the civil law conflict? Is
the individual free when he then obeys the civil law? Moreover, what
if the civil law is enacted by a legislative body in whose election the
individual has had no say? (Locke apparently would not grant universal suffrage, although this point is not wholly clear.) Is the individual then free when he obeys, perhaps contrary to his own choice?
Locke might still hold him to be free, since he has entered into the
contract which is the basis of the society. But in that case the artifi-
ciality of Locke's theory would be hiding the real problem from him.
No doubt a contract would be implicit in the democratic society which
Locke had in mind. It is implicit in the individual's recognition of his
duty to the community, the recognition which gives strength to a
democracy. But a civil society as described by Locke, this group of
free individuals, who have explicitly entered into a compact, is very
different from civil society in its concrete actuality. The latter rests on
much more than contract, and to say that each individual who finds

[11] § 21.

himself in the state is there wholly by contract is to misrepresent the truth.

It must be concluded that the problem of the relations between individual and community is one which Locke does not finally solve. Nevertheless, Locke's individualism is a fact and needs to be stressed. He is first an individualist in so far as he sets as narrow limits as are possible to the state's power. Government can demand the individual's obedience only in limited spheres. Within these spheres its authority is final. But outside them it has no authority. The individual is wholly free, for instance, in his family, or again in his religious life, as long as he does not interfere with the liberty of others. In the same way he can use his leisure in whatever way he desires, and choose whatever profession he desires. But, in the second place, Locke is also individualist in the further sense that he views government as itself an instrument to promote the individual's good. It is true that it seeks the greatest good of the greatest number, 'the public good', and so an occasional individual may find his own good sacrificed. But civil society does not exist to further any other purpose than that of the public good. Locke's individualism is largely a question of emphasis. He puts all his stress on the rights of the individual which should never be sacrificed except in the extreme case in which the freedom of one individual must be curtailed to give freedom to others. There is a sense in which Locke could accept the principle, *Gemeinnutz vor Eigennutz*. He is not afraid of governmental interference in the life of the individual. After all, he was mercantilist in his economic theories and admitted the need for governmental control in trade. And there are other spheres where Locke would consider government could profitably intervene. But if it does so, it intervenes to better the prospects of the greatest number of individuals. In a word, government is an instrument to be used for the good of individuals. The state is made for the individual and not the individual for the state. It is in this sense, more than in any other, that Locke is the champion of individualism.[12]

[12] On this point and generally, compare J. W. Gough, *John Locke's Political Philosophy* (1950), and the introduction to his edition of *The Second Treatise of Civil Government* (1946). On influences upon Locke cf. in particular A. H. Maclean, 'George Lawson and John Locke', *Cambridge Hist. Journal*, 1947, i. 69–77, in which he asserts that a great deal of Locke's argument is to be found in Lawson's *Politica Sacra et Civilis* (1660).

THE RIGHT OF THE MAJORITY*

Willmoore Kendall

☆

When any number of men have . . . consented to make one community or government . . . the majority have a right to act and conclude the rest.[1]

This is Locke's clearest statement of his doctrine regarding what we have called in our Introduction the majority-principle, and it is, be it noted, so phrased as to fit very neatly into our interpretation of the compact. Wherever men live in community with one another, he is saying, the relations between them can be described in terms of an agreement which, in addition to assigning to the whole community that unlimited power which we have examined in the preceding section, assigns to its numerical majority a *right* to make decisions (regarding the use of that power) which are binding upon the minority. The majority-principle is, in a word, implicit in the logic of community life.

It is not only Locke's clearest commitment to the use of the majority-principle, but also the most concise statement of the faith of the majority-rule democrat that the present writer has been able to find in the course of his investigation; and we shall greatly clarify the problem of the present section if we face at once all that it implies. Assuming—as, in the context in which it is claimed, we must assume—that the right to which the statement refers is an ethical right, then it necessarily follows that decisions made by the majority (= action taken by the majority) are in some definable sense ethically right decisions, since, in the absence of convincing proof to the contrary, it is necessary to suppose that there can be no such thing as an ethical right to make an ethically wrong decision. It follows, again, that any decision other than that of the majority is in some definable sense ethically wrong. It follows, yet again, that a decision comes to be right the moment it marshals majority support behind it, and ceases to be right

* Reprinted from *John Locke and the Doctrine of Majority Rule*, Illinois Studies in the Social Sciences, Vol. 26, No. 2 (1941), 112–119, by permission of the University of Illinois Press.

[1] Locke, *Second Treatise*, ch. vii, sect. 95 (cited by chapter and section number).

the moment the "marginal" deliberator switches sides and reduces the erstwhile majority to a minority. And since these corollaries do clearly follow from it, it is to Locke, not to any recent writer, that Professor Friedrich should give credit for a "statement of the majoritarian position" which "avoids all subterfuges."[2]

We shall greatly clarify our problem, too, by facing at once the implications of Locke's proposition about the right of the majority with regard to the questions dealt with in the preceding sections. The individual has, as we have seen, an irrevocable obligation to obey the community of which he is a member; but the majority has a right to act for the community; and the individual's irrevocable duty of obedience thus turns out to be an irrevocable duty to obey the majority. The inalienable rights of the individual are, as we have seen, such rights as may be compatible with the public good of his society, and, as we have further seen, that public good is merely that which the "opinion" and "humour" of the people designate as good; but since the majority of those people have a right to conclude the rest, the inalienable rights of the individual prove to be merely those which the majority of the people have not yet seen fit to withdraw.[3] The "proper interest" of each individual lies in obedience to a law decreed by a legislative which, as we have seen, is presumed to enjoy the confidence of the community; but since the majority can act for the community, and can thus exercise the community's right of revolution and its right to replace the old government with a new one to its liking, the proper interest of the individual becomes merely unquestioning obedience to the will of the majority. Here, in short, is the Rousseauism which is nowhere to be found in the *Contrat social* and the *Gouvernement de Pologne;* and it is a matter of no little interest that Locke, apparently because the platitudes about morals which we have examined in the opening sections of this chapter cannot be squared with such a position, has got off with so little responsibility for the introduction of such notions into modern political theory.[4]

[2] Carl J. Friedrich, "One Majority against Another," *Southern Review*, v (1939), 43. Cf. C. E. Vaughan, *Studies in the History of Political Philosophy before and after Rousseau*, 2 vols. (Manchester: University Press, 1925), I, 166: "This [Locke's statement on the power of the majority] amounts to a blank cheque drawn in favour of the 'the majority,' and eventually filled up either to tens or millions, as fortune may decide."

[3] But cf. Francis G. Wilson, *Elements of Modern Politics* (New York: McGraw-Hill, 1936), pp. 218–219: "Locke's *Two Treatises* put above the rough determination of majority vote the immutable natural rights of man."

[4] Thus Vaughan, who in view of the comment reproduced in n. 2 above, can hardly be accused of having *overlooked* the majoritarian emphasis in Locke's

We now turn to consider the arguments by which Locke supports this proposition.[5]

First Argument. The right to live under a government agreeable to the majority is a natural right of all men—or, in Locke's own language, men have a "native right . . . to have such a legislative over them as the majority should approve and freely acquiesce in."[6] This Locke does not seek to demonstrate; and we need only take notice of its presence in the *Second Treatise* and remind the reader of Ritchie's pleasantry[7] to the effect that the maxim, "No case; talk about the law of nature," plays in the profession of political theory a rôle analogous to that of the maxim, "No case; abuse plaintiff's attorney," in the practice of law.[8]

Second Argument. If the minority refused to be concluded by

---

theory, yet clings to the notion that that theory is "not merely anti-despotic, but also markedly individualist" (*op. cit.*, I. p. 134). "*The Essay of Civil Government*," he writes (*ibid.*), "is . . . an assault . . . upon the very idea of sovereignty. Its shafts are aimed not merely against one particular form of sovereignty—doubtless the most oppressive and the least endurable—but against any form [thus against 'blank cheques' to majorities?], even the mildest, that sovereignty can assume." Locke pleads for toleration for all save atheists and Catholics, and wins a reputation for having exercised "considerable" influence in "advancing the cause of toleration" (Sterling P. Lamprecht, *The Moral and Political Philosophy of John Locke* [New York: Columbia University Press, 1918], p. 152); Rousseau pleads (*Contrat social*, iv. 8) for toleration for all save atheists and Catholics, and Vaughan (*The Political Writings of Rousseau* [Cambridge: University Press, 1915], I, p. 89) accuses him of advocating persecution. Rousseau writes (*op. cit.*, iv. 2) that provided "tous les caractères de la volonté générale sont encore dans la pluralité," I am more free when subjecting myself to the will of the majority than I would have been had I got my way—and wins recognition as a majoritarian! Locke, with no limiting conditions at all, equates the consent of the individual with that of the majority, and wins recognition as an individualist! Cf. Locke, xi. 140: "Governments cannot be supported without great charge, and it is fit everyone . . . should pay out of his estate his proportion for the maintenance of it. *But still it must be with his own consent, i.e., the consent of the majority*" (italics mine).

[5] It is instructive to notice that there is absolutely nothing in the *Contrat social* which can properly be called an argument for majority-right.

[6] xvi. 176. The writer has not attempted to list Locke's arguments in the order in which he introduces them.

[7] David G. Ritchie, *Natural Rights* (London: Swan Sonnenschein and Co., 1895), p. 31.

[8] Cf. Vaughan, *Studies*, I, pp. 140–141: "The answer of Locke is perfectly explicit: Those who make a social contract bind themselves to . . . regulate all their future proceedings by a bare majority: a provision imposed by that accommodating oracle, the law of nature, whose commands form the strangest assortment, ranging from *Thou shalt not kill* to *The odd man shall have the casting vote.*"

the majority, the society would speedily disintegrate; for, he insists, the only alternative is the unanimity-principle (= "nothing but the consent of every individual can make anything to be the act of the whole"[9]); and both because it is frequently impossible to consult everybody[10] and because "variety of opinions and contrariety of interests . . . unavoidably happen in all collections of men,"[11] such a principle would deprive the society of the strength it needs in order to fulfill the purposes for which it was created.[12] In short, "where the majority cannot conclude the rest, there they cannot act as one body, and consequently will be immediately dissolved again."[13]

This we may call the argument from *necessity and expediency*,[14] and the importance it has assumed in subsequent discussion of the case for majority-decisions is the most interesting indication we possess of the need for investigation of the problem by competent theorists. It is open to the following obvious objections:

(a) It is simply not true that a commonwealth must choose between decisions by majority-vote and dissolution after a brief period of experiment with unanimous decisions, since, as Locke must have known very well, the power to make decisions binding upon all of its members may (and often does) become lodged in a minority of the society's members. That is, Locke's dilemma is, in the form in which he states it, a false dilemma.

(b) If it *were* true that the society must choose between dissolution and the lodgment of decision-making power in the majority, this would not constitute a valid argument in favor of the proposition that wherever men have "consented to make a community," the majority have a right to make that community's decisions. Even conceding the inarticulate premise that all commonwealths have a right to continue in existence and to thrive, the most that can be deduced from it is a decision-making right in that part of each commonwealth which is in fact most capable of assuring to it a healthy existence. It is possible to conceive of circumstances in which such a right might, on this showing, vest in the majority, but it is also possible to conceive of circum-

---

[9] viii. 98.
[10] Cf. *ibid.*: "Infirmities of health and avocations of business . . . will necessarily keep many away from the public assembly."
[11] *Ibid.*
[12] *Ibid.*
[13] *Ibid.*
[14] Cf. Wilson, *op. cit.*, p. 64: "Locke in his *Second Treatise* defends majority rule primarily on the ground of expediency, for without it civil society could not endure."

stances in which the majority-principle would conduce directly to the commonwealth's ruin. In such a case (leaving to one side the ever-present possibility of minority-rule) dissolution and majority-rule would appear to be equally undesirable.

For the rest, it seems improbable that the premise, according to which all commonwealths to which men happen at some time to have given their "consent," have a right to continue in existence and to thrive, can be successfully defended.

For all of its absurdity, in the form in which Locke states it, the argument contains the elements of a proposition which—although it still awaits its theorist—deserves (in the present writer's opinion) serious consideration as the point of departure for theoretically sound treatment of the majority-principle. For if, instead of saying that the society must either entrust decision-making power to the majority or face speedy dissolution, he had said that it must either entrust the decision-making power to the majority or cease to be *a society in which all can participate in the making of decisions*, he would not only have enunciated a proposition which cannot be so easily refuted as that which he does put forward, but also would have set his successors in the modern debate about majority-rule a problem worthy of their best speculative efforts.

Third Argument. Denial of the right of the majority to conclude the minority would deprive the commonwealth of its title to govern.[15]

That which begins and actually constitutes any political society is nothing but the consent of any number of freemen capable of majority, to unite and incorporate into such a society [*i.e.*, one in which all necessary power has been given up to the majority]. . . . This is that, and that only, which did or could give beginning to any lawful government in the world.[16]

Here, again, Locke is apparently very close to the idea which we have set forth at the end of our discussion of the second argument, and seems about to say that there are demonstrable differences between a

---

[15] It is interesting to note the use which the members of a minority (in a society governed in accordance with Locke's ideas about majority-rule) might make of one of his pronouncements on absolute monarchy—*e.g.*, vii. 90–91: "Absolute monarchy . . . is indeed inconsistent with civil society, and so can be no form of civil government at all . . . [The absolute prince] being supposed to have all . . . power in himself alone, there is no judge to be found, no appeal lies open to any one, who may fairly and indifferently, and with authority decide, and from whence relief and redress may be expected of any injury or inconveniency that may be suffered from him, or by his order."

[16] viii. 99.

society which does and one which does not make its decisions by majority-vote[17]—and differences which, from the ethical point of view, render the former distinctly preferable. But he does not say this; and since he adds that where the members have "expressly agreed in any number greater than the majority,"[18] that arrangement also is legitimate, it may well be that he does not intend even to imply it. (To stipulate in favor of decision-making by extraordinary majority is, obviously, to stipulate in favor of a *minority-right* to conclude the majority.) In short, the single clear implication of the statement, as it stands, is that any sort of government to which men have at some time consented is lawful, and the safest conclusions seem to be (a) that the *Second Treatise* contains no unequivocal doctrine on this point, and (b) that the passage in question was intended merely as a reiteration of his general doctrine of consent as the basis of lawful government, its apparent emphasis upon majority-right being the result of careless wording.

Fourth Argument. Political bodies, like all other bodies, must move in the direction in which they are impelled by the greater force, and in political bodies the greater force is the will of the majority.

This we may call the argument by analogy, and, like the argument from necessity, it has attracted many subsequent writers. What it amounts to is an insistence that majority-determination in political societies is natural, as it is natural for water to seek its level, for the heavier end of a seesaw to point downward, and (to follow the direction which Krabbe gives to the argument) for the human mind to make that decision to which it is drawn by the more weighty reasons. Its inarticulate major premise, when urged as an argument in favor of

---

[17] It is on this level that Starosolskyj attacks the problem of majority-decisions. His book—the best we have on the subject—is an effort to demonstrate the theoretically necessary differences between what he calls the *Mehrheitsverband* and what he calls the *Herrschaftsverband* (Wolodymyr Starosolskyj, *Das Majoritätsprinzip* [Wein und Leipzig: F. Deuticke, 1916], pp. 22–34). Unfortunately, he defines the *Mehrheitsverband* in such fashion as to exclude any organization in which there exists a crystallized majority—*i.e.*, any organization in which the relations of subordination and superordination have ceased to be "indeterminate" (*ibid.*, p. 33). This means, of course, that the difference between the *Mehrheitsverband* and the *Herrschaftsverband* does not, at the limit, turn at all upon the fact that in the one decisions are made by the majority and in the other by an individual or a minority. Nevertheless, Starosolskyj has pointed the way to an adequate theoretical treatment of the problem, and if his theory could be restated in such fashion as to eliminate the confusion to which we have just directed attention, it might prove useful in the extreme.

[18] viii. 99.

the right of the majority, is that the natural is not only natural but also right.

In Locke's hands the argument consists of the following steps: The motivating force of a community, in virtue of which alone it can act as a community, is the consent (past promise? present support?) of its individual members. Therefore the greater motivating force within it is the consent of the greater number of its individual members, and, at the limit, the consent of one half of those members plus one. If, then, we were to suppose it capable of responding to the force exerted by the smaller number of its individual members, we should have to suppose it different in this respect from all other bodies of which we possess knowledge.[19]

The argument is intensely interesting, if only as a reminder of the justice of Professor Catlin's acknowledgment of indebtedness to the contract theorists;[20] for here, in a paragraph, is the central conception of his admirable *Principles of Politics*. Those familiar with the refinement it has received in Professor Catlin's treatment will, therefore, see at once that it owes its plausibility (in Locke) to a carefully concealed *non sequitur*. The argument is unexceptionable insofar as it asserts that the motivating force of a community is consent—*if* we understand by consent present support rather than past commitment. It is unexceptionable, again, insofar as it asserts that the consent which motivates a community is a consent given (ultimately) by individuals. It is unexceptionable, finally, insofar as it asserts that more consent (for consent *is* additive) generates a greater motivating force than less consent. But it does not follow from these propositions that the consent which motivates a given society at any given moment is that of the greater number of its individual members, unless we are in a position to assume that the members are equally active in giving and withholding their consent, and unless, further, we are in a position to assume that the

---

[19] viii. 96. The language in the text is a free but (the writer believes) faithful paraphrase.

[20] G. E. G. Catlin, *The Principles of Politics* (New York: Macmillan, 1930), p. 169: "Men will become, not fugitive from society, but rebels against it, unless they are permitted to believe that they are acting freely in those things to which they attach most value. Restraint has no theoretical limit, but constraint can be imposed by no prudent statesman without a cautious calculation of his power to enforce it. *The theorists of the seventeenth and eighteenth centuries were, then, quite right in founding the contract upon the possibility of a rebellious attitude of will in every man.* It is not possible to quit society; but it is very possible to be anti-social, and, still more, anti-national, anti-group, impious, unconventional" (italics mine).

consents given and withheld are of equal *intensity*.[21] No spectacle is more familiar in politics than that of a majority's abdication of responsibility for the making of decisions, unless it be that of the ease with which a smaller number of persons with intense convictions can make their consent count for more than that of a larger number of persons who, without joining the politically inactive majority, are yet not prepared, on the particular issue at stake, to offer resistance to the smaller number. The validity of Locke's conclusion rests, therefore, on two hidden premises (equal individual participation in the making of decisions, equal intensity of conviction on each issue to be decided) of whose necessity he reveals no sort of awareness; and we must conclude that that which he declares to be natural is natural only where certain indispensable conditions are satisfied.

If, *per impossible*, we were to waive these objections, and grant for argument's sake that decisions by majority-vote are a natural phenomenon of community life, there would remain the difficulty that we cannot argue from the naturalness of the process by which the majority concludes the minority to a *majority-right* to conclude the minority—or, if the reader prefers, we cannot argue from the one to the other without first demonstrating our title to do so.

Fifth Argument. Individual consents being, in any case, the only rightful title to the exercise of power, the right of the majority flows as a matter of course from the fact that it can point to more consents than the minority.

This, in the opinion of the present writer, is what was really in Locke's mind as he wrote the paragraphs in which he attempts to defend the notion of majority-right, although, admittedly, some exegesis is needed in order to establish its presence in those paragraphs. A man, the argument runs, necessarily surrenders some of his liberty when he subscribes to the compact which makes him a member of a commonwealth.[22] The compact "would signify nothing, and be no compact if he be left free and under no other ties than he was in before in the state of Nature. . . . What new engagement [would there be] if he were no farther tied by any decrees of the society than *he himself thought* fit and did actually consent to?"[23] In consenting to be a

---

[21] Cf. *ibid.*, p. 266: "If all men were equal, or if government were only possible if all men believed themselves to have an equal share, then only majority government (over-riding the 'equal shares' of the minority as a practical expedient) would be feasible."

[22] viii. 97.

[23] *Ibid.* (italics mine).

member of a commonwealth, therefore, he consents beforehand to the acceptance of obligations which he does not himself approve, and it is right that he should do so because such an obligation is implicit in the nature of community life. And the character of the obligation, be it noted, is to be discovered in a situation in which the community, otherwise unanimous (as we are clearly asked to conceive it in the passage cited), is making a demand of the individual to which he is not prepared to give his consent. The compact would be all to the advantage of the individual, thus no compact, if it did not involve a duty on the part of the individual to fulfill the demand, thus also a right on the part of the community to make it, thus also a reciprocal obligation among all the individuals in the community to fulfill such a demand when it happens to be made of them. In other words, that community life to which all the individuals consent is possible on no other basis; and therefore, Locke is saying, "every man, by consenting with others to make one body politic under one government, puts himself under an obligation to every one of that society to submit to the determination of the majority."[24]

Now the thing which Locke's critics have failed to perceive (thus overlooking the major emphasis of his defense of the majority-principle) is that, although he does not assist us with the deduction, the right of the majority to conclude the minority does follow as a matter of course from the right of the community to conclude the individual, *insofar as that right is defended in terms of the community's numerical superiority over the individual.* If one million persons have a right to conclude one because they are a million and he is only one, then there is no logical escape from the conclusion that five hundred thousand and one persons have a right to conclude five hundred thousand persons, and if one does not like the conclusion one must revise one's notions regarding the premise.

In a word, Locke had apprehended—on a half-conscious level—a tremendously important logical relation between the doctrine that the whole people have a right to have their way and the doctrine that the majority have a right to have their way. For either you mean, by the former doctrine, that the people must be really unanimous in order to exert their rightful authority, in which case there will be no one left upon whom it can be exerted, or you mean, as we have gone to some pains to show that Locke always did, that virtual unanimity is as good a title to authority as the people require, in which case you must be

<hr>

[24] *Ibid.*

willing (as Locke was) to go ahead and defend—without any of those "subterfuges" to which Professor Friedrich refers—the majority-principle.

We conclude: (a) that the first, second, third, and fourth of these arguments in favor of majority-right may properly be dismissed as unworthy of serious consideration; (b) that, insofar as he intended to show with his fourth argument that his theory of majority-right is logically implied in his theory of popular sovereignty, he was on safe ground; and (c) that our evaluation of his theory of majority-right must be dictated by our evaluation of his theory of popular sovereignty.

SUGGESTED FURTHER
READINGS

The readings below are divided into seven topics. Works by Locke, in the first section, are arranged in descending order of importance to a consideration of his political philosophy. All other entries are listed by order of publication within each section.

I. WORKS BY LOCKE

The Works of John Locke. London: T. Tegg, 1823. 10 vols. Reprinted, 1963.

Two Treatises of Government (1689). A Critical Edition. Ed. Peter Laslett. Cambridge: Cambridge University Press, 1960. 2nd ed., 1967. Available as a Mentor paperback.

Essays on the Law of Nature. Edited and translated from the original manuscripts and published for the first time by W. von Leyden. Oxford: Oxford University Press, 1954.

Two Tracts on Government. Edited and translated from the original manuscripts and published for the first time by Philip Abrams. Cambridge: Cambridge University Press, 1967.

An Essay concerning Human Understanding (1690). Ed. John W. Yolton. 2 vols. London and New York: Everyman's Library, 1961.

On the Reasonableness of Christianity (1695). Ed. George W. Ewing. Chicago: Henry Regnery Company, 1965.

P. Long. *A Summary Catalogue of the Lovelace Collection of the Papers of John Locke in the Bodleian Library*. Oxford: Oxford University Press, 1959.

II. GENERAL WORKS ON LOCKE AND HIS POLITICAL PHILOSOPHY

Note: A comprehensive bibliography (with some significant omissions) covering all aspects of Locke's thought has recently been published. See Roland Hall and Roger Woolhouse, "Forty Years of Work on John Locke (1929–1969)," *Philosophical Quarterly*, XX (1970), 258–268.

D. J. O'Conner. *John Locke*. New York: Dover Publications, 1967. (Originally published by Penguin Books in 1952.)

Richard I. Aaron. *John Locke*. 2nd ed. Oxford: Oxford University Press, 1955.

J. W. Gough. *John Locke's Political Philosophy: Eight Studies*. Oxford: Oxford University Press, 1950. Corrected reissue, 1956.

Maurice Cranston. *John Locke: A Biography*. New York: Macmillan, 1957.

Richard Cox. *Locke on War and Peace*. Oxford: Oxford University Press, 1960.

M. Seliger. *The Liberal Politics of John Locke*. London: George Allen & Unwin, 1968.

John Dunn. *The Political Thought of John Locke*. Cambridge: Cambridge University Press, 1969.

John W. Yolton, ed. *John Locke: Problems and Perspectives: A Collection of New Essays*. Cambridge: Cambridge University Press, 1969.

III. NATURAL LAW AND NATURAL RIGHTS

Margaret MacDonald. "Natural Rights." Originally published in the *Proceedings of the Aristotelian Society*, XLVIII (1947–48), and reprinted in *Philosophy, Politics and Society*. 1st series. Ed. Peter Laslett. Oxford: Basil Blackwell, 1956. Pp. 35–55.

H. L. A. Hart. "Are There Any Natural Rights?" *Philosophical Review*, LXIV (1955), 175–191.

John W. Yolton. *John Locke and the Way of Ideas*. Oxford: Oxford University Press, 1956.

John W. Yolton. "Locke on the Law of Nature." *Philosophical Review*, LXVII (1958), 477–498.

Raghuveer Singh. "John Locke and the Theory of Natural Law." *Political Studies*, IX (1961), 105–118.

M. Seliger. "Locke's Natural Law and the Foundation of Politics." *Journal of the History of Ideas*, XXIV (1963), 337–354.

Francis Oakley and Elliot W. Urdang. "Locke, Natural Law, and God." *Natural Law Forum*, XI (1966), 92–109.

J. J. Jenkins. "Locke and Natural Rights." *Philosophy*, XLII (1967), 149–154.

C. B. Macpherson. "Natural Rights in Hobbes and Locke." *Political Theory and the Rights of Man*. Ed. D. D. Raphael. London: Indiana University Press, 1967. Pp. 1–15.

Raymond Polin. "The Rights of Man in Hobbes and Locke." *Political Theory and the Rights of Man.* Ed. D. D. Raphael. London: Indiana University Press, 1967. Pp. 16–26.

Jeffrie G. Murphy. "A Paradox in Locke's Theory of Natural Rights." *Dialogue,* VIII (1969), 256–271.

IV. LOCKE'S THEORY OF PROPERTY

Richard Schlatter. *Private Property: The History of an Idea.* London: George Allen & Unwin, 1951. Pp. 151–161.

Melvin Cherno. "Locke on Property: A Reappraisal." *Ethics,* LXVIII (1957–58), 51–55.

C. B. Macpherson. *The Political Theory of Possessive Individualism: Hobbes to Locke.* Oxford: Oxford University Press, 1962. Ch. v, "Locke: The Political Theory of Appropriation." An elaboration and extension of the argument in the article reprinted in this collection.

Jacob Viner. " 'Possessive Individualism' as Original Sin." *Canadian Journal of Economics and Political Science,* XXIX (1963), 548–559. A review of Macpherson.

Sir Isaiah Berlin. "Hobbes, Locke, and Professor Macpherson." *Political Quarterly,* XXXV (1964), 444–468.

Henry Moulds. "Private Property in Locke's State of Nature." *American Journal of Economics and Sociology,* XXIII (1964), 179–188.

David P. Gauthier. "The Role of Inheritance in Locke's Political Theory." *Canadian Journal of Economics and Political Science,* XXXII (1966), 38–45.

Max Milam. "The Epistemological Basis of Locke's Idea of Property." *Western Political Quarterly,* XX (1967), 16–30.

V. OBLIGATION AND THE MORAL CONDITIONS OF SOCIETY

Theodore Waldman. "A Note on John Locke's Concept of Consent." *Ethics,* LXVIII (1957–58), 45–50.

Joseph Tussman. *Obligation and the Body Politic.* New York: Oxford University Press, 1960.

John Plamenatz. *Man and Society.* 2 vols. New York: McGraw-Hill, 1963.

Raymond Polin. "Justice in Locke's Philosophy." *Nomos VI: Justice.* Ed. Carl J. Friedrich and John W. Chapman. New York: Atherton Press, 1963. Pp. 262–283.

Hanna Pitkin. "Obligation and Consent." *American Political Science Review*, LIX (1965), 990–999, and LX (1966), 39–52.

Thomas McPherson. *Political Obligation*. London: Routledge & Kegan Paul, 1967.

John Dunn. "Justice and the Interpretation of Locke's Political Theory." *Political Studies*, XVI (1968), 68–87.

John Plamenatz. *Consent, Freedom, and Political Obligation*. 2nd ed. Oxford: Oxford University Press, 1968. Ch. 2 and Epilogue.

VI. MAJORITARIANISM, INDIVIDUALISM, AND REVOLUTION

Louis Arénilla. "The Notion of Civil Disobedience According to Locke." *Diogenes*, no. 35 (Fall, 1961), 109–135.

Martin Seliger. "Locke's Theory of Revolutionary Action." *Western Political Quarterly*, XVI (1963), 548–568.

Geraint Parry. "Individuality, Politics and the Critique of Paternalism in Locke." *Political Studies*, XII (1964), 163–177.

Henry Moulds. "John Locke and Rugged Individualism." *American Journal of Economics and Sociology*, XXIV (1965), 97–109.

VII. OTHER TOPICS

Merle Curti. "The Great Mr. Locke: America's Philosopher, 1783–1861." *Huntington Library Bulletin*, XI (1937), 107–151.

Walter M. Simon. "John Locke: Philosophy and Political Theory." *American Political Science Review*, XLV (1951), 386–399.

Henry Moulds. "John Locke's Four Freedoms Seen in a New Light," *Ethics*, LXXI (1960–61), 121–126.

Richard Ashcraft. "Locke's State of Nature: Historical Fact or Moral Fiction?" *American Political Science Review*, XLII (1968), 898–915.

———. "Political Theory and Political Reform: Locke's Essay on Virginia." *Western Political Quarterly*, XXII (1969), 742–758.

Frank Marini. "John Locke and the Revision of Classical Liberalism." *Western Political Quarterly*, XXII (1969), 5–18.

Stewart Edwards. "Political Philosophy Belimed: The Case of Locke." *Political Studies*, XVII (1969), 273–293.